McGRAW-HILL PUBLICATIONS IN THE
AGRICULTURAL SCIENCES

LEON J. COLE, CONSULTING EDITOR

STATISTICAL TECHNIQUE

IN

AGRICULTURAL RESEARCH

SELECTED TITLES FROM

McGRAW-HILL PUBLICATIONS IN THE AGRICULTURAL SCIENCES

LEON J. COLE, *Consulting Editor*

Boyle · MARKETING OF AGRICULTURAL PRODUCTS
Brown · COTTON
Cruess · COMMERCIAL FRUIT AND VEGETABLE PRODUCTS
Eckles, Combs, and Macy · MILK AND MILK PRODUCTS
Fawcett · CITRUS DISEASES
Fernald · APPLIED ENTOMOLOGY
Gardner, Bradford, and Hooker · FRUIT PRODUCTION
Gustafson · CONSERVATION OF THE SOIL
Hayes and Garber · BREEDING CROP PLANTS
Heald · MANUAL OF PLANT DISEASES
　　　　INTRODUCTION TO PLANT PATHOLOGY
Hutcheson, Wolfe, and Kipps · FIELD CROPS
Jull · POULTRY HUSBANDRY
Maynard · ANIMAL NUTRITION
Metcalf and Flint · DESTRUCTIVE AND USEFUL INSECTS
Paterson · STATISTICAL TECHNIQUE IN AGRICULTURAL RESEARCH
Rice · THE BREEDING AND IMPROVEMENT OF FARM ANIMALS
Thompson · VEGETABLE CROPS
Waite · POULTRY SCIENCE AND PRACTICE

There are also the related series of McGraw-Hill Publications in the Botanical Sciences, of which Edmund W. Sinnott is Consulting Editor, and in the Zoological Sciences, of which A. Franklin Shull is Consulting Editor. Titles in the Agricultural Sciences were published in these series in the period 1917 to 1937.

STATISTICAL TECHNIQUE

IN

AGRICULTURAL RESEARCH

A Simple Exposition of
Practice and Procedure in Biometry

BY

D. D. PATERSON, B.Sc., B.Sc. (Agric.), Edin.

Reader in Agriculture at the Imperial College of Tropical
Agriculture, Trinidad, B.W.I.

FIRST EDITION

McGRAW-HILL BOOK COMPANY, Inc.

NEW YORK AND LONDON

1939

THE MAPLE PRESS COMPANY, YORK, PA.

PREFACE

Recent advances in statistical method have given the research biologist a new and valuable weapon to aid him in the accurate interpretation of his data. Statistics is a branch of applied mathematics, and a comprehensive understanding of the theory is possible only to those of a mathematical turn of mind. In consequence, a full appreciation of the fundamental mathematics must remain the prerogative of the few. On the other hand, there is no reason why those who are interested in statistics solely as an aid to scientific research should forego the advantages of applying statistical methods to research data derived from any standardized experimental design. The interpretation of the results by means of the appropriate statistical formulas should then become a purely routine operation. The available literature is rather technical in character, and several years' experience with postgraduate students has shown that there is a real demand for a more elementary exposition of statistical technique. This book is an attempt to meet this demand and is essentially the detailed analysis of data from a representative series of experiments typical of some of the commoner statistical problems encountered by the average research worker. In certain examples, the original data have been slightly simplified in order to make it easy to follow the successive stages in the arithmetical calculations. It is hoped that these representative examples may serve as a practical guide to the research worker in the design and interpretation of his experiments. For the student who has to study the subject more deeply, they may even help toward an easier understanding of statistical theory as expounded in the more technical works.

In compiling this handbook, the writer has made liberal use of the relevant literature. To the authors of the various theoretical and practical memoirs consulted, he wishes to express his deep indebtedness. In particular, grateful acknowledgment is made to Professor R. A. Fisher and to his publishers, Messrs. Oliver and Boyd, for permission to reproduce some of the fundamental tables from "Statistical Methods for Research Workers."

TRINIDAD, B.W.I.,
January, 1939.

D. D. PATERSON.

CONTENTS

"I would go further and insist that all biological investigation involves a statistical consideration of the results."

—Sir A. D. Hall, Rothamsted Conferences, 1931

STATISTICAL TECHNIQUE
IN
AGRICULTURAL RESEARCH

CHAPTER I

GENERAL PRINCIPLES

Scientific progress can be largely attributed to a detailed examination of what is happening in nature under a given set of conditions. The material available for examination generally represents the aggregate of a large number of individuals or units with certain fundamental characteristics common to all. The sum total of all the units of any one kind is called, in statistical terminology, the *population*. A population in this sense need not actually exist, but the term may refer to the aggregate of all individuals that might have existed under the specified conditions. For example, in a test of the yield of wheat from a series of plots, the population is the hypothetical one consisting of an infinite number of plots of that particular wheat grown on the same soil type and in the same season. While the individuals in any one population are similar in general type, they are not necessarily identical, and for any particular character under observation, considerable variation among the individual units comprising the population may be anticipated. For example, in data relative to the height of men, the recorded measurements will probably vary over a range of at least 60 to 72 inches. Any quantity or quality liable to show variation from one individual to the next in the same population is termed a *variable*. An individual observation or value of any variable is known as a *variate*.

Observations may be qualitative or quantitative in character. Observations on the petal color of the progeny of a hybrid strain of sweet pea belong to the former category and yield data or

1

growth records in a field experiment to the latter. A further system of classification is the one which distinguishes between continuous and discrete observations. *Continuous* variates are those which can take any value or fractional value within the total range exhibited by the population. *Discrete* variates are those which cannot take fractional values but differ from one another by regular and finite gradations. Germination counts would belong to this latter class of variate as the data would be limited to whole numbers. Quantitative observations more commonly belong to the continuous group of variates. In practice, however, it is not possible to carry out the measurements to an infinitesimal fraction of a value, and even in a continuous series, the recorded variates differ from one another by definite gradations, the size of the gradation being determined by the recognized standards of measurement for the particular character under observation.

In biological research, the variability between the individuals in the population must be looked upon as an integral and unavoidable feature of the material from which observations are made and must be taken into consideration in formulating conclusions. The aim of the research worker is to characterize the population as a whole in order to compare it with other more or less similar populations and to arrive at a correct appreciation of their relative values. It is, of course, entirely inadequate to observe only a single individual from any particular series, as the variate selected may be widely different from the majority of the other variates in the population. Ideally, to obtain an absolutely exact characterization, all the variates should be taken into consideration. This is usually impracticable, as the number of possible variates in most populations is virtually infinity. It is customary therefore to carry out observations or measurements on a representative sample consisting of a sufficiently large number of variates to demonstrate general attributes which are approximately the same as those of the whole population. The larger the number of variates in the sample, the greater are the chances that it will be truly representative of the population as a whole. The consequence is that the data from any particular investigation are often thoroughly formidable and require to be reduced to some simpler form before the human mind can grasp what they actually demonstrate. Statistics is the branch of applied mathematics which deals with the facts and figures accruing from any series of observations and makes it possible to express the results in simple and logical terms that omit no essential feature of the basal data.

CALCULATION OF MEAN AND STANDARD DEVIATION

In the statistical analysis of the data from any series of quantitative observations, two factors are of fundamental importance:

a. The arithmetical average or *mean* of all the readings. This forms the measure of type of the observations as a whole.

b. The amount of variability shown by the variates. The range from the highest to the lowest values gives a rough indication of this, but the most effective measure of variability, *i.e.*, of the dispersion of the variates round the mean, comes from calculating a quantity known as the *standard deviation*.

It is essentially upon these two factors that the statistical interpretation of the data depends. It is only within the last few decades that the dispersion of the variates has been given proper weight in formulating conclusions. Previously, the calculation of the mean values was deemed sufficient statistical elaboration for all practical purposes. The need of taking into consideration the variability factor is probably most easily illustrated by a simple example. In a qualifying examination for a business appointment, a candidate who scored 95, 85, and 45 per cent in the three examinations set would have the same average as a second applicant who gained 80, 75, and 70 marks, respectively. Although they both achieve 75 per cent on the average of all the results, there can be little doubt that, on the available evidence, the second man would be the more reliable individual to appoint to the vacancy. The percentage he gains in each of the examinations is never seriously behind that of his rival nor below the level indicative of sound general knowledge and intelligence. The former candidate, on the other hand, has done exceptionally well in his first two subjects but is very weak in his third. This suggests that either he was lucky in the selection of questions set in the first two papers or that there are some serious gaps in his education. In either case, his general ability remains more open to question. These arguments might be summarized mathematically by calculating for each individual the range from the highest to the lowest percentage obtained. For the former, this amounts to 50 per cent as compared with only 10 per cent in the case of the latter, proving that the latter is much less likely to show sudden excessive aberration from his estimated mean grade of 75 per cent. In the same way, in any series of observations, the accuracy of the mean as a measure of type is largely dependent on the degree of dispersion shown by the variates from which it has been calculated.

The mean, by simple arithmetic, is the sum of all the measurements or variates in a sample divided by the total number of observations recorded. The standard deviation is calculated by taking the square root of the sum of the squares of the deviation of each variate from the mean divided by the total number of variates less one. The deviation of the variates is evaluated by subtracting the mean from each one in turn; the deviation may be positive or negative. If the mean is estimated with sufficient accuracy, the algebraic sum of these deviations will be zero. In calculating the standard deviation, it will be noticed that the sum of the squares of the deviations is divided by a quantity equivalent to the number of variates less one. This divisor has been termed the *number of degrees of freedom.* The use of the number of degrees of freedom in preference to the older system of dividing by the actual number of observations is to the novice one of the most puzzling ideas of modern statistical methods. While the origin of the concept lies in rather abstruse mathematical theory, the basic principle is that the mean square deviation should be evaluated from the number of independent comparisons of the variates with the mean, *i.e.*, on the number of independent deviations. As the mean is calculated directly from the total of the variates, and the algebraic sum of the deviations is zero, it follows that in a sample of n variates, when $n - 1$ deviations have been calculated, the value of the final deviation is fixed. There are therefore only $n - 1$ independent comparisons possible; in other words, the number of degrees of freedom is $n - 1$.

The calculation of the mean and standard deviation is illustrated in the following example, in which observations on the height of the male population in an industrial locality in Lancashire are recorded. A sample of 36 individuals in all was taken.

Example 1.   Calculation of Mean and Standard Deviation.

TABLE 1.—HEIGHT MEASUREMENTS

Height of men, in. (y)	Deviation from the mean ($y - M$)		Deviation^2 ($y - M$)^2
	−	+	
67	1		1
69		1	1
68		0	0
70		2	4
68		0	0
63	5		25
69		1	1
67	1		1
71		3	9
69		1	1
65	3		9
70		2	4
68		0	0
64	4		16
66	2		4
60	8		64
74		6	36
67	1		1
65	3		9
71		3	9
67	1		1
59	9		81
75		7	49
68		0	0
66	2		4
74		6	36
68		0	0
70		2	4
68		0	0
71		3	9
69		1	1
63	5		25
66	2		4
72		4	16
69		1	1
72		4	16
2,448	−47	+47	442

Let y = any one variate.

    n = total number of variates.

    M = mean.

    σ = standard deviation.

    Σ = sum of.

Then, mean,

$$M = \frac{\Sigma y}{n}$$

$$= \frac{2,448}{36} = 68 \text{ in.}$$

and standard deviation,

$$\sigma = \sqrt{\frac{\Sigma(y - M)^2}{n - 1}}$$

$$= \sqrt{442\tfrac{2}{35}}$$

$$= 3.55$$

The sum of the deviations squared, *i.e.*, $\Sigma(y - M)^2$ is generally termed the *sum of squares* or more briefly the S.S. The square of the standard deviation, *i.e.*, the sum of squares divided by the number of degrees of freedom is called the *variance*. The definition of these two terms should be borne in mind, as they recur frequently in the succeeding pages.

NORMAL CURVE OF ERROR

As a preliminary to a working knowledge of the way in which the mean and standard deviation are used in the analysis of experimental data, a little statistical theory will have to be assimilated. It is hoped that the following brief exposition in nontechnical language will provide the novice with sufficient information of the principles upon which statistical methods are based.

Examination of the first column in Table 1 shows that many of the values appear several times, *i.e.*, that many of the individuals measured were of the same height. This makes it possible to group the readings in a frequency table, as shown in Table 2. *Frequency* is a term used to denote the number of variates having the same value or belonging to the same quantitative class.

TABLE 2.—FREQUENCY TABLE OF HEIGHT MEASUREMENTS
RECORDED IN TABLE 1

Height of men, in.	Frequency, *i.e.*, no. of men in each height class
59	1
60	1
61	0
62	0
63	2
64	1
65	2
66	3
67	4
68	6
69	5
70	3
71	3
72	2
73	0
74	2
75	1
Total...............	36

It is obviously possible to give a graphical or geometrical representation of this frequency table by plotting the height along a horizontal scale against the corresponding frequency on a vertical scale. This has been done in Fig. 1*A* resulting in the figure known as a histogram, *i.e.*, one consisting of columns of equal width but unequal height. The total frequency is proportional to the area of the histogram. Even in this small sample, it is evident that the higher frequency values tend to be clustered round the mean, while the low ones are located toward the extremes of the height range represented. This feature is characteristic of many frequency diagrams. As the number of variates in the sample is increased, the tendency is for the outline of the histogram to become more and more regular with a peak at the mean value and a gradually descending range of frequencies on either side of it. In this particular instance, with the unit of measurement of one inch, it will be impossible even in a very large sample for the outline of the histogram ever to develop into a smooth curve. Nevertheless, if we imagine that the unit of measurement is indefinitely reduced to a mere fraction of an inch and an infinitely large number of individuals are included in the sample, the irregular steps of the histogram will ultimately be replaced by a smooth curve known as a frequency curve. Depending on the particular variable under observation, these curves will generally assume one or other of certain recognized

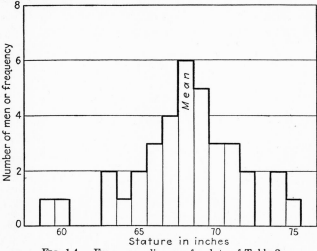

Fig. 1A.—Frequency diagram for data of Table 2.

forms. The commonest form, and the one with which we are immediately concerned, is known as the *normal curve of error* (Fig. 1B). The normal curve has not been obtained from actual records but is an abstraction conceived by mathematicians who have studied this variation factor and have constructed the equation which accurately defines the theoretical curve.

The normal curve is symmetrical about a vertical line—the mean. The total frequency is represented by the area enclosed between the curve and the horizontal axis. In any such curve, the width at the base, *i.e.*, at its widest point, measures the range of the variates from the highest to the lowest value. The normal curve has an infinite range from $+\infty$ to $-\infty$. The general form of the curve indicates the amount of variability in the population; the more upright the curve and the steeper its slope, the smaller is the variation. The deviation of any variate is equivalent to the distance along the horizontal scale that the particular value is from the mean.   It is from the sum of squares of all such deviations that the standard deviation—the statistic which measures the dispersion of the variates—is calculated.   It is evident that the flatter the curve the higher will be the value of the standard deviation.

From the normal curve of error for any normally distributed population, it is possible to estimate the probability of selecting from the population at random a variate above or below any specified value.   Before explaining how this is done, it is advis-

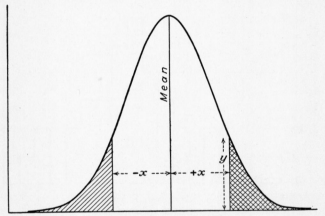

Fig. 1*B*.—The normal curve.

able to define exactly what is meant by the term probability. In mathematics, *probability* is expressed quantitatively by the ratio of the number of times an event happens to the total number of trials carried out.   For example, in tossing a coin a large number of times, one would expect a head to appear on the average once out of two trials.   The probability of obtaining a head is therefore 0.5.   Similarly, in throwing a die, the chances of obtaining a four are one in six, *i.e.*, the probability is 0.16.   An alternative method of expressing this is to give the odds against the event occurring.   Odds against are given by the ratio of the number of times an event is not likely to occur to the number of times it is likely to occur.   The odds against obtaining a four in throwing a die are therefore 5 to 1, and of obtaining a head in tossing a coin are 1 to 1.   In statistical work, probability is the form normally used. This is usually expressed as $P =$ some decimal fraction.

In the normal curve, an ordinate raised at a distance or deviation $+x$ from the mean divides the curve into two unequal sections (Fig. 1*B*). The area of the smaller portion, shown cross shaded in the diagram and generally termed the tail, is proportional to the frequency represented by all variates exceeding $M + x$ in value. The total area enclosed by the curve is proportional to the total frequency of the population. Therefore the probability of selecting purely at random a variate exceeding $M + x$ in value is given by the ratio of the area of the tail to that of the whole curve.

Mathematicians have proved that, for all normal curves, the ratio $\dfrac{x}{\sigma}$ (where x represents any deviation from the mean and σ the standard deviation) bears a definite relation to the proportion into which the normal curve is divided by an ordinate raised at a deviation x from the mean. Thus, for a deviation equivalent to σ, *i.e.*, when $\dfrac{x}{\sigma} = 1$, the area of the tail is always 0.15866 of the whole curve, and for $\dfrac{x}{\sigma} = 2.5$, the area of the tail is 0.00621 of the whole. In statistical work, a deviation of $-x$ is often quite as significant as one of $+x$, and it becomes necessary to determine the probability of selecting values outside the range $M \pm x$. The probability will then be equivalent to the proportionate area which the two tails—cut off by ordinates raised at deviations of $+x$ and $-x$ from the mean—are of the whole curve. As the curve is symmetrical, the tails are of equal area, and the probability is just twice that for a deviation greater than x in one direction only. Tables have been prepared which show for practically all values of $\dfrac{x}{\sigma}$ the proportionate areas cut off by the two ordinates raised at deviations of $+x$ and $-x$ from the mean. These are tables of the *probability integrals.*

Fisher's Table of x, a copy of which is reproduced as Table I in the Appendix, is a modified form of the table of the probability integrals. Table of x shows, for the normal curve, the theoretical values of $\dfrac{x}{\sigma}$ for certain selected probabilities from 0 to 1. It is proposed to use the data in Example 1 to demonstrate the way in which this table may be of utility in the interpretation of experimental results. In this example, the mean height is 68 inches and the standard deviation is 3.55 inches. It is desired to estimate the probability of selecting at random from the population an individual greater than, for example, 72 inches in height. In solving this problem, it is necessary to assume, that the population is normally distributed and that the figures given for the mean and the standard deviation are true estimates of these statistics.

As $M = 68$ and $M + x = 72$, $x = +4$ in.

$$\frac{x}{\sigma} = \frac{4}{3.55} = 1.127$$

Reference to the Table of x shows that the nearest recorded value of $\frac{x}{\sigma}$ is 1.126391 for $P = 0.26$. The probability of obtaining a $+$ or $-$ deviation greater than 4 inches is 0.26 approximately. In this problem, we are interested only in the chances of obtaining a deviation greater than $+4$ inches, *i.e.*, in a deviation in a positive direction only. The required figure is therefore exactly half that quoted on the table, so that the probability of selecting at random an individual greater than 72 inches in height is approximately 0.13.

Similarly, it might be necessary to estimate the chances of selecting an individual outside a certain range, say $M \pm 2\sigma$, *i.e.*, outside the range 60.9 to 75.1 inches. The deviation here is 2σ so that $\frac{x}{\sigma} = 2$. The nearest reading on the table is 1.959964 for $P = 0.05$. The chances of selecting a variate outside this range are only 1 in 20. The odds against selecting such a variate are therefore 19 to 1.

Population is a term used to define the aggregate of a number of similar individuals, real or hypothetical, and it is seldom possible to utilize the whole population in evaluating the mean and the standard deviation. Instead of this, a reasonably large number of individuals is selected at random as a representative sample of the whole population, and this sample is used to provide estimates of the mean and the standard deviation. The calculated values of these statistics are therefore only approximations to the true values required, and it is necessary to ascertain whether these estimates may be regarded as reliable or not.   The most important question is the accuracy of the mean as the measure of type of the population.   This could be tested by taking a large number of similar samples, working out the mean for each, and observing whether these individual means showed a wide variation or not. Such a method would be extremely laborious and is quite unnecessary, as it is possible to calculate, from the data of the original sample, the dispersion or standard deviation likely to be shown by such a series of means.

STANDARD ERROR

If σ is a standard deviation calculated from a sample of n variates, the standard deviation of the mean of the sample $= \dfrac{\sigma}{\sqrt{n}}$. This value is really an estimate of the dispersion or standard deviation of a hypothetical population of means.   It is generally termed the *standard error*.   It is important to distinguish between σ, the standard deviation of the individual variates and the standard error $\dfrac{\sigma}{\sqrt{n}}$.

It is not always practicable to prove that the population from which any sample of variates has been selected is normally distributed.   Statisticians have shown, however, that, even in populations not quite normal in distribution, there is a tendency for the means evaluated from a series of large samples to be normally distributed.   The larger the individual sample, the greater is the likelihood of normality in the distribution of the means.   It is fairly safe to assume that, for large samples, the published tables for the normal curve can be used to determine the probability that the mean of the sample will differ by more than any specified quantity from the true mean of the population.

Suppose in Example 1 it is desired to ascertain the probability that the true mean lies outside the range of 67 to 69 inches.   The standard error is $\dfrac{3.55}{\sqrt{36}} = 0.591$.   Limits of 67 to 69 inches represent a deviation of ± 1 from the mean value of 68 inches.   As we are concerned here with the dispersion of means and not of variates, the value of $\dfrac{x}{\sigma}$ required for use in conjunction with the Table of x is $\dfrac{x}{\text{standard error}}$ or $\dfrac{1}{0.591} = 1.692$.   The nearest reading from the Table of x is 1.695398 for $P = 0.09$. The chances that the true mean lies outside the limits of **67 to 69** inches are less than 1 to 10.

Research data are generally recorded in order to carry out a comparison of two more or less similar variables A and B and to ascertain whether there is or is not any fundamental difference between them. There will consequently be two series of measurements or samples, one from A and the other from B. From each of these samples an estimate of the mean and the standard deviation of the respective populations is obtained. Any real difference between A and B will be reflected in the mean values as measures of type of the populations as a whole. However, an apparent difference between the means may be due either to some fundamental difference between the variables A and B or to unavoidable variation between two similar samples from the same population—generally termed errors of random sampling. Statistical treatment is necessary to ascertain to which of these two factors the difference between the means can be rightly attributed.

STATISTICAL SIGNIFICANCE

In the statistical comparison of the means, the assumption is first made that the two samples come from the same population, *i.e.*, that there is no real difference between A and B. As already explained, a number of similar samples from the same population will give estimates of the mean differing slightly from one sample to the next. These estimates tend to be normally distributed, and a measure of their dispersion is available if the standard errors are calculated. It is furthermore true that, if a number of such sample means are recorded in pairs and the difference between each pair tabulated, the differences also will be normally distributed. The standard errors can be used to provide an estimate of the dispersion of such a series of differences. As the differences are normally distributed, this estimate of the standard error of the difference between any pair of sample means can be used in conjunction with the Table of x to assess the probability of obtaining such a difference from samples of the same population. If the probability is very small, the assumption can be safely made that the samples do not belong to the same population, *i.e.*, that there is some fundamental difference between the variables A and B. The difference is then termed *significant.* If, on the other hand, there is a fairly reasonable probability that a difference of the recorded magnitude could be obtained from parallel samples of the same population, the difference is termed *nonsignificant* and is attributed entirely to errors of random sampling.

Before giving an example of the practical application of this technique, it is necessary to quote the equation for calculating the *standard error of the difference between two means.*

Let E_A = standard error of the mean of sample A.

E_B = standard error of the mean of sample B.

D = difference between the two means, *i.e.*, $M_A - M_B$.

Then standard error of the difference $E_D = \sqrt{E_A^2 + E_B^2}$.

Example 2.—As a sequel to the observations on the height of men in Lancashire (Example 1), a similar sample was taken from the industrial population of Yorkshire. The results were as follows:

Series	Mean height, in.	No. of variates (n)	Standard deviation
A. Lancashire............................	68.0	36	3.55
B. Yorkshire............................	66.5	36	2.34

The difference between means is 1.5 inches. Can a difference of this magnitude be regarded as significant or not?

$$E_A = \frac{3.55}{\sqrt{36}} = 0.591$$

$$E_B = \frac{2.34}{\sqrt{36}} = 0.390$$

Standard error of the difference $E_D = \sqrt{0.591^2 + 0.390^2}$
$$= 0.708$$

Therefore

$$\frac{x}{\sigma}, \text{ i.e., } \frac{\text{difference } D}{E_D} = \frac{1.50}{0.708} = 2.12$$

The nearest reading of $\frac{x}{\sigma}$ from the table is 2.17009 for $P = 0.03$. This proves that in only 3 out of 100 times would a difference exceeding 1.5 inches be obtained purely by chance. This would appear to be satisfactory proof that the difference is significant and that the male population from the locality sampled in Lancashire is slightly taller than that from a similar locality in Yorkshire.

It is necessary to emphasize that this proof is not absolute, as in some 3 per cent of such trials, a difference of this magnitude would be obtained purely as a result of errors of random sampling. The particular data tested might by chance belong to this 3 per cent. The general question arises, "What level of probability would be considered adequate proof of significance?" The standard suggested by Fisher—and the one that is normally adopted—is that a probability less than 0.05 can be accepted as sufficient proof that the figure tested represents a real difference between the variables. This is equivalent to odds exceeding 19 to 1 against the conclusion being a false one, which is undoubtedly a reasonable guarantee of accuracy. This division at $P = 0.05$, or as it is sometimes termed, at the 5 per cent point, is, of course, wholly arbitrary, and it is open to each research worker to decide for himself what value of P will provide adequate assurance of the correctness of the conclusions. The lower the value of P, the greater will be the certainty that conclusions based on significant differences are correct but, at the same time, the larger will be the risk of classifying certain real differences as nonsignificant. It is necessary to try and select a level of P which most effectively balances the risk of falsely asserting significance against that of overlooking any real difference, and for this purpose, the 5 per cent point is generally considered to be satisfactory.

Reference to the Table of x (Table I in the Appendix) shows that for $P = 0.05$ the tabulated value of $\frac{x}{\sigma} = 1.959964$ or approximately 2.0. If we accept Fisher's standard for determining significance,

$$\frac{D}{E_D} \text{ must be greater than 2.0.}$$

$$D > 2 \times E_D$$

A significant difference will therefore be one that is greater than twice its standard error. This makes it possible to apply a rapid test of the significance of the results without reference to the

Table of x. In Example 2, the standard error of the difference between means is 0.708. Twice this quantity is 1.416; the difference is 1.5 inches and is therefore significant.

SAMPLING

It should be clear from the preceding discussion that statistical analysis is merely a simple test, based on sound mathematical hypothesis, by means of which the chances of reaching a false conclusion from any series of observations may be limited to any desired level of probability. This probability is evaluated by using certain calculated statistics in conjunction with the table of the probability integrals or the Table of x. The statistics are calculated from the observed data and as these data form only a sample of the whole population, the statistics are only estimates of the required values. The accuracy of the conclusions is therefore dependent on correct sampling, and there are certain precautions which must be observed in selecting a sample.

a. The population from which the sample is drawn should be homogeneous. The individual variates must all belong to the same general type.

b. The sample must be a random one. This means that the individual variates which make up the population must be independent of one another and must each have an equal chance of being selected. For instance in Example 1, if many of the individuals measured were relatives, the variates could not be regarded as independent, and the sample would not be strictly random. Furthermore, if the men were all taken from one village, the individuals in other villages in industrial Lancashire would have no chance of being included, and the sample would be representative, not of the industrial population as a whole, but only of the section domiciled in a particular village.

c. The normal curve is reached by assuming an infinitely large population and an infinitely small unit of measurement. In practice the unit is generally made whatever is convenient or customary. Particularly in small samples, it is important to remember that the unit selected should be considerably smaller than the difference which it is desired to measure.

d. It is only when the number of variates included in the sample is relatively large that it can be safely assumed that the distribution of the variates or even of the means is likely to approach the normal.

ANALYSIS OF SMALL SAMPLES

In certain types of research, *e.g.*, in field experiments, it is impracticable to include a large number of variates or replicates. "Student" has pointed out that, when the sample is small, the statistical tables for the normal curve do not validly apply. The smaller the sample, the larger is the difference likely to be between the sample mean and that of the true population, and the greater are the chances of an incorrect interpretation of the results from the use of the table of the probability integrals. "Student" has worked out for small samples the distribution of a quantity z. "Student's" z^* is a quantity representing the difference between the sample mean and the true mean of the population expressed in terms of the calculated standard deviation, *i.e.*,

$$z = \frac{\text{deviation of mean}}{\text{estimated standard deviation}}$$

From this distribution, "Student's" Table of z has been completed to show the values, corresponding to the probability integrals, that can be correctly applied when the sample is small.

The more modern development of this table is Fisher's Table of t, and it is proposed to limit further discussion here to the use of the t table in the statistical analysis of small samples. t is a quantity representing the difference between the sample and the population means expressed in terms of the standard error,

$$t = \frac{\text{deviation of mean}}{\text{estimated standard error of sample mean}}$$

When a statistical comparison is being made between the means of two small samples, this expression for t resolves into

$$\frac{\text{Difference between sample means}}{\text{Estimated standard error of this difference}} = \frac{D}{E_D}$$

A copy of the Table of t will be found in the Appendix (Table II). The values of t recorded are for probabilities from 0.01 to 0.9 and for estimates of the standard errors based on any number of

* This z should not be confused with Fisher's z referred to later on in the text.

degrees from 1 to 30, and for ∞. The values for ∞ are, of course, identical with those quoted in the Table of x for the same probability, for, in an infinitely large sample, the normal curve is reached once again.   In any analysis, the required value of t from the table is the reading corresponding to the total number of degrees of freedom from which the standard error occurring in the denominator has been evaluated.   The first column (n) shows the number of degrees of freedom to which the values on the same line refer.   As the values of t for n exceeding 30 are only slightly greater than those of the normal curve, *i.e.*, for $n = \infty$, it can be assumed that for degrees of freedom over 30, the table of values for the normal curve applies approximately.

Example 3. Determination of Significance of a Difference between Means of Small Samples.—Table 3 gives the weight of chicks at 7 weeks of age as recorded from two samples A and B of 10 chicks each.   In Series A the chicks had been reared in confinement and in B on open range.   It is desired to ascertain from these data which method of maintenance, A or B, is the better one to use.

The data (Table 3) yield a calculated value of t of 1.92.   In determining the probability that the difference between means is significant, the corresponding theoretical value from the table has to be looked up.   The standard error of the difference is based on 9 degrees of freedom from each sample or a total of 18 degrees of freedom for the whole data.   The table reading required will be the one opposite $n = 18$.   The nearest readings are 1.734 for $P = 0.1$ and 2.101 for $P = 0.05$.   The probability that a difference of this magnitude could be obtained by chance lies between 0.1 and 0.05.   On the accepted standard for a significant difference, $P < 0.05$, this would not be considered adequate proof that the difference was a real one.   The conclusion would therefore be that the alternative methods of rearing the chicks have produced no difference in their rate of growth.

An alternative popular method of arriving at the same result is as follows: A significant difference is one that gives a greater calculated value of t than the corresponding reading from the table for $P = 0.05$.   Therefore for a difference to be significant,

$$\frac{D}{E_D} > t \text{ (from the table)}$$

$$D > t \times E_D$$

Applying this formula to the data of Example 3, the reading of t

for $n = 18$ and $P = 0.05$ is 2.101. A significant difference is one greater than $2.101 \times 1.04 = 2.185$. The difference between means is only 2 ounces and therefore nonsignificant.

TABLE 3.—CALCULATION OF STANDARD ERROR

Series A				Series B			
Wt. of chicks, oz.	Mean wt.	Deviation from mean	Deviation²	Wt. of chicks, oz.	Mean wt.	Deviation from mean	Deviation²
		− +				− +	
9	$^{13}\!\%_{10} = 13$	4	16	8	$^{11}\!\%_{10} = 11$	3	9
17		4	16	15		4	16
14		1	1	11		0	0
13		0	0	11		0	0
15		2	4	9		2	4
10		3	9	12		1	1
11		2	4	11		0	0
13		0	0	10		1	1
13		0	0	9		2	4
15		2	4	14		3	9
130		−9 +9	54	110		−8 +8	44
		0				0	

$$\sigma_A = \sqrt{54\!/_9} = 2.45 \qquad \sigma_B = \sqrt{44\!/_9} = 2.21$$

Standard error, $E_A = \dfrac{2.45}{\sqrt{10}}$ Standard error, $E_B = \dfrac{2.21}{\sqrt{10}}$

$$= 0.77 \qquad\qquad = 0.70$$

Standard error of the difference between means,

$$E_D = \sqrt{0.77^2 + 0.70^2}$$
$$= 1.04$$

difference between means, $D = 13 - 11 = 2$ oz.

$$\frac{D}{E_D} = \frac{2}{1.04} = 1.92$$

ANALYSIS OF CORRELATED SAMPLES—"STUDENT'S" METHOD

It is sometimes possible to reduce the effects of random sampling errors by utilizing some known relationship between the variates of the two series A and B. For example, in comparing the height of men and women, variation in the data due to heredity will tend to be less if the measurements represent height figures for brothers and sisters instead of entirely unrelated individuals. In order to take full advantage of such a relationship between the variables, it is necessary to tabulate the variate for A against the corresponding one for B, *e.g.*, brother vs. sister, and modify the statistical procedure in accordance with the method evolved by "Student." As the chicks in Series B (Example 3) were known to be the offspring of the same parents as those in Series A in the order shown from 1 to 10, these data may be used to illustrate "Student's" method of analysis. The first step is to tabulate, for each pair of chicks of the same family, the difference in weight due to the alternative methods of rearing the birds and then from these individual differences to evaluate the standard error of the mean difference directly.

Example 4.—Determination of Significance of Mean Difference by "Student's" Method.

TABLE 4

Weight of chicks, oz.		Difference in weight between chicks of same parentage, $A - B$		Mean difference	Deviation from mean difference		Square of deviation
Series A	Series B						
		−	+		−	+	
9	8		1	$+^{2}\%_{10} = +2$	1		1
17	15		2			0	0
14	11		3			1	1
13	11		2			0	0
15	9		6			4	16
10	12	2			4		16
11	11		0		2		4
13	10		3			1	1
13	9		4			2	4
15	14		1		1		1
		−2	+22		−8	+8	44
		+20			0		

Standard deviation of differences $= \sqrt{4\frac{4}{9}} = 2.21$

Standard error of mean differences $= \dfrac{2.21}{\sqrt{10}} = 0.70$

The mean difference $= 2$

$$t = \frac{D}{E_D} = \frac{2}{0.70} = 2.857$$

a correct idea of the relative dispersion of the different variables directly from the calculated values of the standard deviations. The units of measurement may be entirely different in the various experiments, and the figure for the standard deviation must be considered in relation to the size of the mean from which it has been determined. For example, a deviation of 2 from a mean of 10 is exactly equivalent, as regards variation, to one of 8 from a mean of 40. For comparative purposes it is customary to express the standard deviation as a percentage of the mean from which it has been calculated. In this form, it is termed the *coefficient of variation*.

The data from Example 2 have been used to calculate the coefficient of variation in the two series *A* and *B*.

Series	Mean height, in.	Standard deviation	Coefficient of variation, per cent
A	68	3.55	$\frac{3.55}{68} \times 100 = 5.22$
B	66.5	2.34	$\frac{2.34}{66.5} \times 100 = 3.52$

The dispersion of the variates round the mean is therefore distinctly greater in Series *A* than in Series *B*.

PROBABLE ERROR

This is a statistic that was formerly used as the measure of the dispersion of the variates round the mean. Its value is $0.67449 \times$ standard deviation, calculated in the ordinary way. The probable error is such that, in the normal curve, ordinates raised at deviations from the mean equivalent to plus and minus the probable error divide the curve along with the mean ordinate into four equal sections or quarters. Such ordinates are therefore termed quartiles. In determining the significance of a difference between mean values, the normal criterion is twice the standard error; this is roughly equivalent to three times the probable error of the mean. The term, probable error, is rather misleading as the quantity does not represent the most probable mistake likely to occur in any series of observations. Fisher states that its only recommendation is its frequent use. Today, it has been largely superseded by the standard deviation, and mention of the probable error has been made here only because it occurs frequently in many of the older books on statistics and may consequently create some confusion among students not familiar with the term.

SHORT METHODS OF COMPUTATION

When the number of variates is limited and the observations are recorded as integers containing only one or two digits, and the mean is a whole number, the direct method of calculating the standard deviation by squaring and summing the individual deviations does not entail an excessive amount of arithmetic. In most statistical problems, however, the number of readings is large, the mean is rarely an integer, and the variates often include three or more digits. Under these circumstances, the routine arithmetic can be greatly reduced by modifying the arithmetical technique. It is proposed to describe some of these alternative methods of computation and to indicate the type of data to which each one is particularly appropriate. It should be clearly understood that it is only the arithmetical procedure that is changed and that the final estimate of any statistic will not be altered. These alternative methods must not be regarded as providing mere approximations to the desired values. In fact, when the mean is not a whole number, they may even eliminate the fractional errors that would otherwise be unavoidable in tabulating the deviations, and tend therefore to be more rather than less accurate than the direct method. It is proposed to use the relatively simple data from Example 3 to exemplify some of the short methods commonly adopted in statistical computation.

Example 5.—Assumed-mean Method of Calculating Standard Deviation.

Procedure.—Instead of calculating the true mean of the variates, an approximate or assumed mean is selected arbitrarily from a rapid survey of the data. From this assumed mean, the deviations and deviations squared are evaluated and summed. It facilitates the rapid and accurate estimation of these deviations if a whole number, preferably a multiple of 10, is chosen as the assumed mean. The assumed mean need not necessarily approximate to the true mean, but on the other hand, the closer it is to the true mean the smaller in the aggregate will be the

This variable-squared method is of benefit when the mean is an inexact decimal and when the variates do not include more than three digits. When the variates contain more digits than this, their squares run to over six figures and are cumbersome to work with; and then the assumed-mean method becomes preferable.

Decimal Fractions.—When the unit of measurement necessitates the inclusion of decimal fractions in tabulating the data, undesirable inaccuracies in the routine arithmetic may be avoided if the variates are multiplied by the lowest power of 10, say 10^n, that will eliminate the decimal. When the statistical calculations are completed, it is easy to revert to the original units by dividing the calculated statistics by the same power of 10. It is possibly advisable to add the rider that for statistics representing squared values, *e.g.*, the variance, the correct divisor will be 10^{2n}.

Short Methods of Computing Standard Error.—The key to most tests of significance is the standard error or the standard error of the mean difference. In evaluating either of these statistics, it is generally advisable to leave the simplification of the preliminary statistical expressions to the end. Thus in Example 3, there is no need to work out the individual values of σ for the two series; the standard error of the difference between means is most easily calculated from the respective variances.

$$E_D = \sqrt{\frac{54 + 44}{9 \times 10}} = 1.04 \text{ (as originally calculated)}$$

In certain types of statistical analysis, the standard errors of the two means are identical. Under those conditions,

$$E_D = \sqrt{2} \times \text{standard error (of either mean)}$$

or, assuming that the two samples have the same number of variates, n,

$$E_D = \sqrt{\frac{2 \times \text{variance of either variable}}{n}}$$

In many problems, the total of the variates forms just as good a measure of type as the mean. It is often simpler to test the significance of a difference between totals instead of between means. This can be easily effected as the formula for the standard error of the total of n variates is known to be $\sigma \times \sqrt{n}$. The technique is an exact parallel to that used for mean differences, and the final conclusion will be exactly the same, whichever method is adopted. In Example 3, the respective standard errors of the two totals of Series A and B are

$$\sqrt{\frac{54 \times 10}{9}} \quad \text{and} \quad \sqrt{\frac{44 \times 10}{9}}$$

and the standard error of the difference between these two totals is

$$\sqrt{\frac{54 + 44}{9}} \times 10 = 10.4$$

This is just 10 times the standard error of the difference between means as calculated in Example 3. The difference between totals must also be exactly 10 times the difference between means, so that the value of $\frac{D}{E_D}$ as calculated from the totals of each series is exactly the same as from the means, and the t test as applied to the totals will therefore lead to the same conclusions.

BASIC FORMULAS*

Standard Deviation.

a. *By Direct Method of Calculation.*

$$\text{S.S.} = \Sigma(y - M)^2$$

$$\sigma = \sqrt{\frac{\Sigma(y - M)^2}{n - 1}}$$

$$\text{Variance} = \frac{\text{S.S.}}{n - 1} = \sigma^2$$

where S.S. = sum of squares.

σ = standard deviation.

$n - 1$ = number of degrees of freedom,

b. *By Assumed-mean Method of Calculation.*

Let

$$\text{Assumed mean} = M_a$$

$$M = M_a + \frac{\Sigma(y - M_a)}{n}$$

* The notation is as in Example 1.

taking into account the sign $+$ or $-$ of $\Sigma(y - M_a)$

$$\text{C.F.} = \frac{[\Sigma(y - M_a)]^2}{n}$$

$$\sigma = \sqrt{\frac{\Sigma(y - M_a)^2 - \text{C.F.}}{n - 1}}$$

where M = mean.

M_a = assumed mean.

C.F. = correction factor.

c. *By Variable-squared Method.*

$$\text{C.F.} = \frac{(\Sigma y)^2}{n}$$

$$\sigma = \sqrt{\frac{\Sigma y^2 - \text{C.F.}}{n - 1}}$$

Standard Error.

Standard error of a mean of n observations,

$$E = \frac{\sigma}{\sqrt{n}} = \sqrt{\frac{\text{variance}}{n}} = \sqrt{\frac{\text{S.S.}}{n(n - 1)}}$$

Standard error of a total of n observations,

$$E_t = \sigma \times \sqrt{n} = \sqrt{\text{variance} \times n}$$

Standard Error of a Difference.

a. *General.*

Standard error of the difference between the means of two samples A and B containing n_1 and n_2 observations, respectively,

$$E_D = \sqrt{E_A^2 + E_B^2} = \sqrt{\frac{\text{variance of } A}{n_1} + \frac{\text{variance of } B}{n_2}}$$

When standard error of each sample is the same, *i.e.*, when $E_A = E_B = E$, then

$$E_D = \sqrt{2} \times E = \sqrt{2 \times \frac{\text{variance}}{n}}$$

Standard error of the difference between the totals of two samples A and B,

$$E_D = \sqrt{\text{variance of } A \times n_1 + \text{variance of } B \times n_2}$$

b. Correlated Series.—If y_1 and y_2 represent corresponding variates in two correlated series, each containing n observations,

$$\text{Mean difference, } D = \frac{\Sigma(y_1 - y_2)}{n}$$

$$\text{Standard error of the mean difference, } E_D = \sqrt{\frac{\Sigma(y_1 - y_2 - D)^2}{n(n - 1)}}$$

By variable-squared method of calculation,

$$E_D = \sqrt{\frac{\Sigma(y_1 - y_2)^2 - \frac{[\Sigma(y_1 - y_2)]^2}{n}}{n(n - 1)}}$$

Statistical Significance.

a. When the number of degrees of freedom does not exceed 30, a significant result is one in which $\frac{D}{E_D} > t$ as recorded in the Table of t for $P = 0.05$ and $n =$ the total available number of degrees of freedom of the observed data.

b. When the degrees of freedom exceed 30, a significant result is one in which $\frac{D}{E_D} > x$ as recorded in the Table of x for $P = 0.05$. This test is approximately equivalent to accepting, as significant, values of $\frac{D}{E_D}$ exceeding two.

c. Alternatively, the probability that any result is nonsignificant may be determined by locating on the appropriate table the reading of t or of x equivalent to the calculated value of $\frac{D}{E_D}$ and noting the corresponding value of P given at the head of the table.

The statistical analysis of a very wide range of experimental data depends on the correct application of these fundamental formulas. The elementary student of statistics should make himself thoroughly familiar with their application to the simple examples cited before proceeding to the more advanced sections of the book. Without this preliminary grasp of the general principles, the student's progress in applied statistics will be "in shallows and in miseries."

CHAPTER II

ANALYSIS OF VARIANCE

In the last chapter the calculations have been limited to the estimation and comparison of statistics from not more than two samples or series. It is seldom that research data are as simple as this. In a single problem, many distinct series or groups of similar variates may be included. In these more complex examples, it is advisable to carry out a detailed statistical analysis of the combined readings from all series in order to obtain a single estimate of the standard deviation based on all the available data.

The total dispersion of the data from such a composite sample represents the combined effect of two distinct factors:

a. The variation shown by the variates within each series or, in other words, the unavoidable errors of random sampling.

b. The variation shown by the means of the different series in which the data can be correctly grouped.

If the contributory sources to the total dispersion are all independent, the sum of squares from the complete data will be equal to the aggregate of the sums of the squares from each of these contributory sources. The process by means of which the total variance in a composite sample is accurately apportioned among the different factors known to be responsible for its gross value has been termed the *analysis of variance*.

Example 7.—Analysis of Variance in Its Simplest Form.

The total dispersion or sum of squares (Table 8) is 118. As the sum of squares is estimated from 20 variates, it will have 19 degrees of freedom. This total sum of squares has now to be split up into its components, *viz.*, the variation within series and the variation between series. The first component has already been calculated in Example 3. The total of all the deviations squared for Series *A* is 54 and for Series *B* is 44, giving an aggregate sum of squares within series of 54 + 44 or 98. This

31

sum of squares has 9 degrees of freedom from each series or a total of 18 degrees of freedom.

TABLE 8.—DATA FROM EXAMPLE 3 FOR WEIGHT OF CHICKENS

Series	Weight of chicks, oz.	General mean	Deviation from mean − +		Square of deviations
A	9	$240/20 = 12$ oz.	3		9
	17			5	25
	14			2	4
	13			1	1
	15			3	9
	10		2		4
	11		1		1
	13			1	1
	13			1	1
	15			3	9
B	8		4		16
	15			3	9
	11		1		1
	11		1		1
	9		3		9
	12			0	0
	11		1		1
	10		2		4
	9		3		9
	14			2	4
Total........	240		−21　+21 0		118

The variation between series depends on the dispersion shown by the means of the series relative to the general mean of the complete data. The appropriate calculations are appended:

Series	Mean of series	General mean	Deviation from general mean − +		Square of deviations
A	13	12		1	1
B	11		1		1
Total........					2

The deviations in the latter calculation are not deviations of single variates but of the means of 10 variates. To obtain a value representing the aggregate dispersion of the 10 variates in each sample, it is necessary to multiply by 10 the square of the deviations as calculated from the means. The sum of squares between series is therefore $2 \times 10 = 20$. As only two deviations were used in its determination, this sum of squares has only 1 degree of freedom. The complete analysis of variance can now be drawn up.

TABLE 9.—ANALYSIS OF VARIANCE

Factor	S.S.	Degrees of freedom	Variance, *i.e.*, $\dfrac{\text{S.S.}}{\text{degrees of freedom}}$
Total..........................	118	19	
Between series.................	20	1	20.0
Within series, *i.e.*, error.........	98	18	5.44

The within-series variance measures the unavoidable variation between similar units in the material or population from which the data have been collected, and the square root of this value provides the best estimate of the standard deviation. As it is from the standard deviation that the standard errors of the means of series are calculated, the within-series variance is generally termed the *error variance*. Thus

$$\sigma = \sqrt{5.44}$$

Standard error of the mean of Series A or B = $\sqrt{\dfrac{5.44}{10}}$

Standard error of the difference between the means of A and B =

$$\sqrt{\frac{5.44 \times 2}{10}} = 1.04$$

To be significant, the difference between the means must be greater than $t \times 1.04 = 2.101 \times 1.04 = 2.185$, where t is the reading from the Table of t (Table II in Appendix) for $P = 0.05$ and $n = 18$, *i.e.*, for the number of degrees of freedom of the error variance. As the difference between the means of A and B is only $13 - 11$ or 2 ounces, it is not significant.

The following points should be noted. The whole of the available data have been used to provide an estimate of the standard deviation, which can be validly applied to determine the standard errors of the means of any of the component series. As these series contain the same number of variates, their standard errors are identical, and the standard error of the difference between the means is therefore $\sqrt{2} \times$ the standard error of any one. Furthermore, the aggregate sum of squares and the aggregate degrees of freedom must be exactly equal to the total sum of squares and degrees of freedom, as independently evaluated. This forms a useful method of checking the arithmetic. The between-series variance is often termed the *treatment variance*, as it is the result of differences in treatment, either natural or artificial, to which the groups of variates have been subjected. When the treatments are complex, the treatment variance may in turn have to be split up into so many component variances in order to complete the analysis of the data.

The short methods of computation can be used with advantage in the calculation of the various factors in the analysis of variance. Using the same data, the evaluation of the total and the treatment sums of squares by the variable-squared method is given in Table 10, and the assumed-mean method has been adopted in the next example.

The only point in the calculation of Table 10 that might require further elucidation is the division of the sum of the squares of the treatment totals by 10. In Series A, there are 10 variates belonging to a group having an average weight of 13 ounces. For the series as a whole, irrespective of the dispersion shown by the individual readings within the group, the sum total of the squares of the variates is 10×13^2. This is equivalent to $10 \times \left(\dfrac{T_i}{10}\right)^2 = \dfrac{T_i^2}{10} = \dfrac{130^2}{10}$, as calculated. Similarly for Series B, the required sum of the squares of the variates for the series as a whole is

$$10 \times 11^2 = \frac{110^2}{10}.$$

The division by 10 is therefore merely a correction for the fact that the aggregate, and not the individual values, of 10 variates has been used in calculating the squares. The process is a parallel one to the multiplication by 10 when the means of the series are used in determining the deviations, as in the original calculations.

TABLE 10.—ANALYSIS OF VARIANCE BY THE VARIABLE-SQUARED METHOD

Series or treatments	Wt. of chicks, oz. (y)	Square of variates (y^2)	Treatment total (T_t)	Square of treatment total $(T_t)^2$
A	9	81		
	17	289		
	14	196		
	13	169		
	15	225		
	10	100		
	11	121		
	13	169		
	13	169		
	15	225	130	16,900
B	8	64		
	15	225		
	11	121		
	11	121		
	9	81		
	12	144		
	11	121		
	10	100		
	9	81		
	14	196	110	12,100
Total........	240	2,998	240	29,000

$$\text{C.F.} = \frac{(\Sigma y)^2}{n}$$
$$= \frac{240^2}{20} = 2,880$$
$$\text{Total S.S.} = 2,998 - 2,880$$
$$= 118$$
$$\text{Treatment S.S.} = \frac{29,000}{10} - 2,880 = 20$$

The division of the total variance to its two components— the within- and the between-series variances—exemplifies a simple but very common form of the analysis of variance and one that can be applied to a wide range of experimental observations.

TABLE 11.—NITROGEN CONTENT OF 6 FODDER GRASSES

Fodder grass	Sample	Nitrogen percentage (y)	Assumed mean (Ma)	Deviation		Total deviation for each grass		Square of deviations	Square of total deviation for each grass	Check on arithmetic. S.S. within duplicate samples
				−	+	−	+			
Elephant grass	I	1.29	110		19		37	361 } 685	1,369	$685 - \dfrac{37^2}{2} = 0.5$
Elephant grass	II	1.28			18			324		
Uba cane	I	1.12			2		3	4 } 5	9	$5 - \dfrac{3^2}{2} = 0.5$
Uba cane	II	1.11			1			1		
Guatemala grass	I	1.07		3		8		9 } 34	64	$34 - \dfrac{8^2}{2} = 2.0$
Guatemala grass	II	1.05		5				25		
Guinea grass	I	1.26			16		20	256 } 272	400	$272 - \dfrac{20^2}{2} = 72.0$
Guinea grass	II	1.14			4			16		
Coimbatore cane	I	1.08		2		8		4 } 40	64	$40 - \dfrac{8^2}{2} = 8.0$
Coimbatore cane	II	1.04		6				36		
Pará grass	I	1.41			21		50	441 } 1,282	2,500	$1{,}282 - \dfrac{50^2}{2} = 32.0$
Pará grass	II	1.49			29			841		
		14.34		−16 } +110				2,318	4,406	115.0
				94						
General mean		1.178								

(*Explanation is at foot of page 37.*)

Basal data relating to such divergent subject matter as soil moisture determinations, germination percentages, chemical analyses, meteorological records, etc., will often lend themselves to this particular technique. In the following example it has been adopted as a test of the accuracy of the sampling method used in the selection of material for chemical analyses from a number of varieties of fodder grass. Duplicate samples were taken from each grass, and the nitrogen percentages were determined in the laboratory. Statistical evaluation was applied to ensure that the variation within the duplicates was small enough to show up any real differences between the grasses in regard to their nitrogen content.

TABLE 12.—ANALYSIS OF VARIANCE

Factor	S.S.	Degrees of freedom	Variance
Total	1,581.7	11	
Treatment	1,466.7	5	293.3
Error	115.0	6	19.2

As there are six varieties, there will be 5 degrees of freedom for the treatments. The within-variety or error sum of squares

Procedure.—To eliminate the decimals, the percentage figures from the chemical analysis have been treated as if multiplied by 100. Deviations and deviations squared from an assumed mean of 110 have then been evaluated for each variate and for each grass.

$$\text{Mean} = M_a + \frac{\Sigma(y - M_a)}{n} = 110 + \frac{94}{12} = 117.8$$

$$\text{C.F.} = \frac{[\Sigma(y - M_a)]^2}{n} = \frac{94^2}{12} = 736.3$$

$$\text{Total S.S.} = 2,318.0 - 736.3 = 1,581.7$$

There are 12 readings in all or a total of 11 degrees of freedom.

$$\text{Between-variety or treatment S.S.} = \frac{4,406}{2} - 736.3 = 1,466.7$$

In calculating this component, the *total* deviation of the two samples of each variety was squared; hence it is necessary, before subtracting the correction factor, to divide the sum of these squares by two.

is the third and final component and must be equal to the difference between the total and the treatment sum of squares or 1,581.7 − 1,466.7 = 115.0, with 6 degrees of freedom. In the last column of Table 11, this component has been evaluated independently.

THE F TEST FOR COMPARING COMPONENT VARIANCES

In any analysis of variance, if the treatment variance is approximately the same as or less than the error variance, it is logical to assume that the difference between the treatments is of the same order as the differences between individuals of the same class. This is equivalent to stating that any apparent difference between treatments is due solely to the errors of random sampling. If, on the other hand, the treatment variance is considerably greater than the error variance, it follows that the difference between series must also be greater than that normally found among variates in the same class, indicating that there is some fundamental difference between the series. *When several different series or treatments are included in the data, the Table of t and the error variance may not validly be used to estimate significant differences between the treatment means, unless the treatment variance is significantly greater than the error variance.* This is most easily determined by calculating the ratio $\dfrac{\text{larger variance}}{\text{smaller variance}}$, a value generally denoted by the letter F. The treatment variance will normally be the larger one and the error variance the smaller one. In any particular analysis, the larger the calculated value of F, the more certain is it that the two variances concerned are significantly different, showing that there must also be a significant difference between the treatments, as typified by their respective means. Tables of F, based on its sampling distribution, are available and record the theoretical values of F for probabilities of 0.05 and 0.01. As these theoretical values vary with the number of degrees of freedom n_1 and n_2 of the two variances from which the calculated value of F has been determined, it is necessary, in referring to the table, to ascertain the reading of F corresponding to the appropriate values of n_1 and n_2, where n_1 represents the number of degrees of freedom of the larger variance. In the Table of F, the values of n_1 are tabulated along the top of the table and of n_2 down the left-hand side. The reading required is the one in the column corresponding to the number of degrees of freedom n_1 of the larger variance and on the line corresponding to the number of degrees of freedom n_2 of the smaller variance. A calculated value of F which exceeds the reading of F for $P = 0.05$ is significant, but if it fails to attain this level, apparent differences between treatments must be regarded as nonsignificant and attributed to errors of random sampling. Obviously, a calculated value of F which exceeds the appropriate reading for $P = 0.01$ is highly significant. A concrete example should enable the student to grasp what this technique involves in practice.

For the data of Table 12, the required calculations would be as follows:

Factor	Variance	Degrees of freedom	F By calculation, *i.e.*, $\dfrac{V_1}{V_2}$ where $V_1 > V_2$
Treatment...............	293.3 (V_1)	5 (n_1)	15.28
Error....................	19.2 (V_2)	6 (n_2)	

The Table of F (Appendix, Table VI) for $n_1 = 5$, $n_2 = 6$, and $P = 0.05$ records a reading of $F = 4.39$ and for $P = 0.01$ a reading of 8.746. The calculated value of F exceeds either of these, so that the difference between the treatments is not only significant but is also highly significant, as determined on a probability considerably less than 0.01.

As the F test has given a positive result, the error variance may now be used to compare the mean nitrogen percentages of the various grasses:

$$\sigma = \sqrt{19.2}$$

Standard error of the mean percentage for each grass =

$$\sqrt{\frac{19.2}{2}} = 3.10$$

Standard error of the difference between two such means =

$$\sqrt{\frac{19.2 \times 2}{2}} = 4.38$$

It is advisable at this stage to revert to the true units of measurement by dividing by the factor originally used to eliminate the decimals from the statistical calculations. In this example, the factor was 100 so that the standard error of the difference between the mean nitrogen percentages of the various grasses is 0.0438. The reading of t for $n = 6$ and $P = 0.05$ is 2.447, and differences between treatment means greater than $2.447 \times 0.0438 = 0.107$ are therefore significant.

This value has now to be used to assess the relative merits of the six fodder grasses by comparing the varietal means in all possible combinations, two at a time, in order to determine the significant differences. When a number of different treatments are concerned, this is most easily effected by tabulating the means in ascending order and entering alongside each the amount of the difference from the previous value, thus:

Fodder grass	Mean nitrogen, %	Difference from previous value
Pará grass..............	1.450	
Elephant grass...........	1.285	0.165
Guinea grass............	1.200	0.085
Uba cane..............	1.115	0.085
Guatemala grass.........	1.060	0.055
Coimbatore cane.........	1.060	0.00

Any difference or cumulative difference greater than 0.107—the critical difference as already calculated—proves a significant increase over varieties lower down on the list. On this basis, Pará grass is significantly better than any of the other grasses. Elephant grass is better than the remaining four except guinea grass, which in turn is significantly better than the Guatemala grass and the Coimbatore cane. There is no significant difference between the last three varieties listed.

Another very effective method of summarizing the results is to express the treatment means as a percentage of any standard or control treatment. Using guinea grass here as the control, the results, again arranged in ascending order, might be expressed as shown in Table 13.

The standard error of each mean, as shown in the penultimate column, has also been expressed as a percentage of the control. Its value is $\dfrac{\sqrt{19.2/2}}{1.200} = 2.58$ per cent. A difference between the percentage values greater than $2.58 \times \sqrt{2} \times 2.447 = 8.9$ is significant. In most examples, especially when the number of degrees of freedom of the error variance exceeds 10, the critical difference may be taken as equivalent to three times the standard error of the treatment mean, since the significant difference is $t \times \sqrt{2}$ times the standard error and $t \times \sqrt{2}$ is approximately three. It is now very easy to classify the treat-

TABLE 13.—SUMMARY OF RESULTS

Fodder grass	Mean nitrogen, %	Mean, % of control	Classification
Pará grass.................	1.450	121 ± 2.58	Very good
Elephant grass.............	1.285	107 ± 2.58 ⎫	Good to average
Control—guinea grass........	*1.200*	*100 ± 2.58* ⎬	
Uba cane..................	1.115	93 ± 2.58 ⎭	
Guatemala grass............	1.060	88 ± 2.58 ⎫	Poor
Coimbatore cane...........	1.060	88 ± 2.58 ⎭	

ments into those significantly better, equal to, or worse than the control, as shown in the table.

In some problems, there may be no convenient standard treatment, or the control may be so different from the rest of the treatments as to be unsuitable as a basis of comparison. Some authorities prefer to express the results as a percentage of the general mean of all the variates, as shown below:

TABLE 14.—SUMMARY OF RESULTS

Fodder grass	Mean nitrogen, %	Mean; % of general mean	Classification
Pará grass.................	1.450	123	Very good
Elephant grass.............	1.285	109	Good
Guinea grass..............	1.200	102 ⎫	Average
General mean..............	*1.178*	*100* ⎬	
Uba cane..................	1.115	95 ⎭	
Guatemala grass............	1.060	90 ⎫	Poor
Coimbatore cane...........	1.060	90 ⎭	

The standard error of the general mean, which is computed from all the variates, is less than the standard error of any treatment mean, and it is advisable to take this into account in comparing the various treatments with the general mean.

From the analysis of variance table, the standard error of the general mean is $\sqrt{\dfrac{1.92}{12}}$, and remembering to revert to the original units by dividing by 100, the critical difference for comparing any treatment mean with the general mean is

$$\frac{\sqrt{(19.2/2) + (19.2/12)} \times 2.447}{1.178} \times \frac{100}{100} = 6.95,$$ expressed as a

percentage of the general mean. The classification is much the same as that obtained by comparing the treatments with the control, but the second method has made it possible to segregate the elephant grass into a class by itself, intermediate between the Pará grass and the average grade.

These alternative methods of elaborating significant differences have been discussed at some length, because experimental reports are full of examples in which a valid statistical analysis of the data has been effected, but the final summary of the results leaves much to be desired. The sole object of statistical evaluation is an accurate and intelligible appreciation of the information supplied by the data. Even in experiments involving a large number of treatment comparisons, a clear statement of conclusions should offer no difficulty provided an efficient technique is used for grading the treatment means in accordance with the statistical tests.

THE z TEST

The F test is merely a recent version of the older and more familiar z test as inaugurated by Fisher. As there may be some readers who have got accustomed to and prefer to use the older form, it is advisable here to give a brief account of the z test and to show how the Tables of F may be derived from the Tables of z. Fisher's z is equivalent to half the difference between the Napierian or hyperbolic logarithms* of the variances it is desired to compare, *i.e.*,

$$z = \frac{1}{2} \log_e \left(\frac{\text{variance}_1}{\text{variance}_2}\right)$$

where variance_1 is the greater, and the number of degrees of freedom of the two variances are n_1 and n_2, respectively.

z is normally distributed, and tables have been compiled to show, for probabilities of 0.05 and 0.01, the theoretical value of z

* Napierian logarithms are tabulated in the Appendix (Table V).

for different levels of n_1 and n_2. A copy of the 5 per cent Table of z is reproduced in the Appendix (Table III). The variances are significantly different when the calculated value of z exceeds the reading from the Table of z corresponding to the appropriate values of n_1 and n_2. In applying the z test to the data of Table 12, the required calculations would be as follows:

Factor	Degrees of freedom	Variance	$\log_e$* of variance	z by calculation, *i.e.*, $\dfrac{\text{difference between logs}}{2}$
Treatments.....	5 (n_1)	293.3	5.6812	1.3631
Error...........	6 (n_2)	19.2	2.9549	

* Napierian logarithms are tabulated in the Appendix (Table V).

The reading from the Table of z for $n_1 = 5$ and $n_2 = 6$ is 0.7394. z by calculation is much greater than this, so that the difference between the class means is definitely significant, which is exactly the conclusion previously obtained by the use of the F test.

The Table of F was originally compiled in order to eliminate the necessity of looking up the Napierian logarithms, a somewhat finicky operation. Now

$$z = \frac{1}{2} \log_e \left(\frac{\text{variance}_1}{\text{variance}_2}\right)$$

and

$$F = \left(\frac{\text{variance}_1}{\text{variance}_2}\right)$$

so that F represents the number whose Napierian logarithm is equal to $2z$. For instance, the reading of z in the above example was 0.7394; twice this value is 1.4788. This last number is the Napierian logarithm of 4.388, which is the reading of F obtained originally in applying the F test. The two tests therefore are bound to give identical results. The F test is admittedly the simpler one to apply. On the other hand, if the student is to keep *au fait* with recent literature on agricultural research, it is important for him to be equally familiar with either method of procedure. For this reason, in the succeeding examples the z test has occasionally been used in preference to the F test.

AFFINITY BETWEEN THE *z* AND *t* TESTS

It has been demonstrated that the F and z tests are alternative methods of determining whether the treatment groups of variates differ significantly from one another. When only two treatments are concerned, they must test whether there is a significant difference between the two treatment means. But the significance of the difference between two treatment means may also be determined by calculating $t = \dfrac{D}{E_D}$ and comparing this value with the appropriate one from the Table of t. It follows that, with a single pair of treatments, t and z (or F) are testing the same quantity D, and, if statistical methods are to be regarded as efficient, they must give exactly the same answer. It will be found that this is true in practice, so that, when only two treatments are concerned, the application of both tests is a work of supererogation, as they are bound to lead to precisely the same conclusion. In these circumstances, the easier one to evaluate from the data should be used.

As an illustration of the truth of these statements, it is proposed to test the following data, taken from Table 9, by all three methods (F, z, and t).

Factor	Degrees of freedom	Variance	Treatment mean, oz.
Between-series A and B.........	1	20.0	Series A = 13
Within-series A and B..........	18	5.44	Series B = 11

$$\begin{cases} F = \dfrac{20}{5.44} = 3.676. \\[2mm] \text{Reading from Table of } F = \mathbf{4.414} \\[2mm] (P = 0.05,\ n_1 = 1,\ n_2 = 18) \end{cases}$$

$$\begin{cases} z = \dfrac{2.9957 - 1.6938}{2} = 0.6509. \\[2mm] \text{Reading from 5 per cent } z \text{ Table} = \mathbf{0.7424} \end{cases}$$

$$t = \frac{13 - 11}{\sqrt{(5.44 \times 2)/10}} = 1.30$$

The nearest reading from the Table of t is 1.330 corresponding to a probability of 0.2. By all three tests, the difference of 2 ounces between the mean treatment values is nonsignificant. Also, the excess of the readings of F and z over their respective calculated values is of a degree that one would normally associate with a probability between 0.1 and 0.2. It may safely be assumed that the three tests are in complete agreement.

INTERACTIONS

The division of the total variance to the treatment and error components is the simplest form of the analysis of variance. The experimental design has often to be made much more complex in character so as to test simultaneously the effect of several distinct treatment series and their reaction on one another. In such comprehensive experiments it is necessary to split up, in the correct proportions, the total treatment variance among the various components to which it can be correctly allocated. This detailed statistical analysis is an essential preliminary to an accurate appreciation of the factors responsible for any apparent difference between the treatments or combinations of treatments under observation. The statistical methods employed introduce no new principles; they represent merely an extension of the procedure already described in connection with simple data. There is however, one term—interaction—which possibly requires a little explanation. Its exact significance will be most easily comprehended by discussion of a concrete example. Consider a field experiment in which the yield data for two varieties of wheat, A and B, have been recorded for two seasons, I and II, the first season being a wet one and the second a dry one. If both varieties are types that thrive under dry weather conditions, higher yields in the second season than in the first could be expected and the percentage increase in A would be approximately the same as in B. The relative difference between the varieties would be maintained, the best one in season I maintaining its superiority in season II. In other words, the response of the two varieties to the change in climatic conditions would be similar. On the other hand, if A is a type that does well in dry weather, but B is one which is at its optimum in a humid environment, the chances are that the yield of A will rise and the yield of B will fall from the first to the second season. The relative yields of the two varieties will be considerably altered, and if the difference in response to the change in season is sufficiently great, the better yielder in the first season may even become the lower yielder in the second. The increase in *A* will be more or less compensated for by the decrease in *B* so that there will not be a marked difference between the total yields for each season. Under these circumstances, the varieties have reacted differently to a change of climatic conditions, and in statistics, this difference in response in one series of treatments to a change in a second series is termed the *interaction*, which in this example would be defined as the interaction of season on variety. In such cases, where one series of treatments is superimposed on a second, it is necessary to take into consideration, not only the straightforward treatment comparisons, but also the way in which the combinations of treatments react on one another. In the above example, there are really 2 × 2 or 4 treatments, *viz.*,

Variety *A* in Season I
Variety *A* in Season II
Variety *B* in Season I
Variety *B* in Season II

In a complete analysis of such data, the total variance between the four treatments would have to be split up as follows:

   a. That portion ascribable to differences between varieties *A* and *B*.
   b. That portion ascribable to differences between seasons I and II.
   c. That portion ascribable to differences resulting from the response of each variety to the seasons.

The first two components are generally termed the *main effects* as they are evaluated from the average or total differences between one series of treatments for all levels of the second series. The third component represents the *interaction;* in this example, the interaction of season on variety. The *F* or *z* tests when used to compare the variety variance *a* with that for error will determine whether there is a significant difference between the two varieties, as estimated from their mean yields for the two seasons' records. The same test applied to the seasonal variance *b* will show which season, I or II, has been the better for the wheat crop in so far as the average response of only two varieties is capable of indicating this. Finally, a significant interaction variance, c, as determined by the F test, proves that the varieties have responded differently to the change in season and permits a valid comparison of the mean varietal yields for each season. From this comparison it should be possible to specify which is the better variety to sow in each type of season.

An interaction of this type is termed a first-order interaction; it shows how changes in one factor X react to changes in a second factor Y or vice versa. Where three distinct series of comparisons are being tested, X, Y, and Z, there will be first-order interactions of X on Y, X on Z, and Y on Z and also a second-order interaction showing how X behaves under various combinations of Y and Z, how Y responds to changes of X and Z, or how Z responds to changes of X and Y. The calculation and utility of interaction variances are exemplified in the succeeding examples.

Example 8.—In a feeding experiment with tropical dairy cattle, 40 cows known to be of approximately the same yield potentiality were divided into eight groups of five and one ration allocated to each group. The experiment was planned on the *factorial* system, a term denoting a design in which two or more series of treatments or factors are included in all possible combinations. In this experiment, four types of roughage were being tested in conjunction with two rates of concentrate ration, necessitating, on a 4×2 factorial arrangement, eight distinct treatment combinations. These are detailed along with the results in Table 15.

The error sum of squares measures the dispersion of the yield data within the different groups of five animals fed on one particular ration. The eight individual rations are complex in nature resulting from the comparison, in a single experiment, of four types of roughage and two quantities of concentrate (0 and 1). The sum of squares for rations should therefore be resolved into its components, *viz.*, that owing to differences in the

a. Roughage ration $\Big\}$ main effects.
b. Concentrate ration

c. Interaction of concentrate with roughage.

$$\text{S.S. roughage} = \frac{90^2 + 110^2 + 115^2 + 165^2}{10} - \frac{480^2}{40}$$
$$= 305 \text{ with 3 degrees of freedom}$$

$$\text{S.S. concentrate} = \frac{242^2 + 238^2}{20} - \frac{480^2}{40}$$
$$= 0.4 \text{ with 1 degree of freedom}$$

The interaction of roughage and concentrate accounts for the balance of the ration sum of squares and degrees of freedom.

S.S. interaction, $= 342.8 - (308 + 0.4) = 37.4$ with $7 - (3 + 1)$
(concentrate $\times$ roughage) or 3 degrees of freedom

TABLE 15.—MEAN YIELD OF MILK IN PINTS PER DAY PER ANIMAL

Reference no. of animal in group	Ration							
	Straw		Hay		Herbage		Legume silage	
	$A*$	$B\dagger$	$A*$	$B\dagger$	$A*$	$B\dagger$	$A*$	$B\dagger$
1	8	8	12	10	12	11	14	17
2	10	9	13	12	10	9	17	19
3	11	8	11	10	13	11	13	17
4	10	10	14	11	12	11	14	16
5	7	9	10	7	14	12	17	21
	46	44	60	50	61	54	75	90
	90		110		115		165	

* With concentrates.
† Without concentrates.

With concentrates 242 ⎱ grand total 480
Without concentrates 238 ⎰

$$\text{Total S.S.} = 8^2 + 10^2 + \cdots 16^2 + 21^2 - \frac{480^2}{40}$$
$$= 424 \text{ with 39 degrees of freedom}$$

$$\text{Ration S.S.} = \frac{46^2 + 44^2 + 60^2 + \cdots 75^2 + 90^2}{5} - \frac{480^2}{40}$$
$$= 342.8 \text{ with 7 degrees of freedom}$$

$$\text{Error S.S.} = 424 - 342.8$$
$$= 81.2 \text{ with 32 degrees of freedom}$$

The F test is used to compare each of the component variances with the error variance to ascertain whether any of the treatments has had a significant effect on the results. As the variance of the concentrates is actually less than that of error, this factor is obviously nonsignificant and the calculation of this F would be a work of supererogation. The calculated values of F for the other two factors—roughage and interaction—are greater than the corresponding theoretical values at the 1 per cent point, and the differences are therefore highly significant. This makes it valid to use the t test to compare (a) the milk yields obtained from the

TABLE 16.—ANALYSIS OF VARIANCE

Factor	S.S.	Degrees of freedom	Variance	F (by calculation)	Table reading of F ($P = 0.01$)
Total..............	424.0	39			
Roughage..........	305.0	3	101.7	40.68	4.51 approx.
Concentrate	0.4	1	0.4		
Interaction: Concentrate × roughage..	37.4	3	12.5	5.00	4.51 approx.
Error..............	81.2	32	2.5		

different types of roughage and (b) the proportionate yields from these fodders with and without concentrates. For the evaluation of the roughage, the comparable yields are the totals obtained from the 10 cows fed on each of the fodders, irrespective of the concentrate ration used. These totals are as follows:

	Pints
Straw......................................	90
Hay.......................................	110
Herbage...................................	115
Silage....................................	165

A difference between any two of these totals greater than

$$\sqrt{2.5 \times 10 \times 2} \times 2 = 14.14 \text{ pints is significant.}$$

Straw is the poorest and silage very markedly the best roughage of the four. This is generally true whether or not concentrates are used in addition to the coarse fodder.

The nonsignificant variance for quantity of concentrate leads to the rather unexpected conclusion that the addition of concentrate to the ration has not, *on the average,* resulted in an increase in milk yield. The significant interaction permits the use of the error variance to compare the following treatment totals from which the interaction sum of squares was estimated:

Treatment factor	Straw	Hay	Herbage	Silage
With concentrates.................	46	60	61	75
Without concentrates..............	44	50	54	90

Differences between these totals greater than

$$\sqrt{2.5 \times 5 \times 2} \times 2 = 10 \text{ are significant.}$$

It would appear that the addition of concentrates improves the value of the hay and herbage relative to straw: without concentrates these two fodders just fail to give a significantly higher yield than that obtained from straw. The legume silage, with or without concentrates, is better than any of the other rations. Furthermore, with the silage the concentrates actually depress the milk yield, presumably on account of a ration too rich in protein. This fact also explains why in the analysis of variance the effect of concentrates is apparently nil. With the first three forms of roughage, concentrates tend to increase yields, but with the silage, they depress the yields; hence, in considering the average effect of concentrates for all four fodders, the variance is nonsignificant.

This example effectively illustrates the advantage of examining two or more factors in a single experiment and resolving the analysis of variance into its ultimate components. In this feeding trial, the inclusion of both roughage and concentrate has made it possible to ascertain which is the best fodder and also to show for each one the exact economy of adding concentrates to the ration.

DIRECT CALCULATION OF AN INTERACTION

When only two values representing the same number of variates are concerned in the determination of any particular component of the analysis of variance, the sum of squares for this factor can be most easily calculated directly from the difference between these values. If T_A represents the total of all the n variates in the first series and T_B the corresponding total for the n variates in the second series, then by the variable-squared method,

$$\text{Required S.S.} = \frac{T_A^2 + T_B^2}{n} - \frac{(T_A + T_B)^2}{2n}$$
$$= \frac{(T_A - T_B)^2}{2n}$$

Thus in the last example,

$$\text{S.S. for concentrates} = \frac{(242 - 238)^2}{40} = 0.4$$

This method can be applied to components of the analysis of variance in which more than two factors are concerned, provided the totals from an equal number of variates are taken in pairs in all combinations, the differences between each pair squared, these squares summed, and then the sum divided by the total number of variates in the data. Thus
S.S. roughage =

$$\frac{(90 - 110)^2 + (90 - 115)^2 + (90 - 165)^2 + (110 - 115)^2 + (110 - 165)^2 + (115 - 165)^2}{40} =$$

305 (as originally calculated)

In examples of this type where a relatively large number of differences have to be calculated from an even number of totals, it is simpler to assess the sum of squares from the differences between all combinations of these totals, two at a time. Thus
S.S. roughage =

$$\frac{[(90+110) - (115+165)]^2 + [(90+115) - (110+165)]^2 + [(90+165) - (110+115)]^2}{40} = 305$$

This arithmetical technique can be further extended to calculate the interaction sum of squares between roughage and concentrates. The totals which determine the value of the interaction are tabulated below:

Treatment factor	Straw	Hay	Herbage	Silage
With concentrates................	46	60	61	75
Without concentrates.............	44	50	54	90
Difference.....................	+ 2	+10	+ 7	−15

The interaction really tests whether the addition of the concentrates to the ration has or has not had approximately the same effect in each of the four fodders. If there is no interaction effect, the difference between straw with and without concentrates will be exactly the same as that between hay with and without concentrates. Comparing these data, the addition of concentrate has changed the yield from *a.* the straw ration by $46 - 44 = +2$ units.

b. the hay ration by $60 - 50 = +10$ units.

The effect of the concentrate has been much more marked in the case of the hay ration; in other words there is a differential response or interaction when the influence of concentrates on the hay and straw rations is compared. The magnitude of this interaction or difference in response is proportional to $2 - 10$ or -8 units. Similarly, by taking the fodders in all the other possible combinations, two at a time—straw and herbage, straw and silage, hay and herbage, etc.—any difference in response to concentrate can be measured. The sum of the squares of these values divided by 40 will be the interaction sum of squares. Thus, S.S. interaction =

$$\frac{(+2-10)^2+(2-7)^2+(2--15)^2+(10-7)^2+(10--15)^2+(7--15)^2}{40}$$

$$= 37.4 \text{ (as originally calculated)}$$

The alternative method of calculation in which differences are assessed from the required totals taken in all possible pairs is also applicable.

S.S. interaction =

$$\left.\begin{array}{l} \{[(46 + 60) - (44 + 50)] - [(61 + 75) - (54 + 90)]\}^2 \\ + \{[(46 + 61) - (44 + 54)] - [(60 + 75) - (50 + 90)]\}^2 \\ + \{[(46 + 75) - (44 + 90)] - [(60 + 61) - (50 + 54)]\}^2 \end{array}\right\} \div 40$$

$$= \frac{20^2 + 14^2 + 30^2}{40} = 37.4$$

ANALYSIS OF DATA DIVIDED INTO SUBUNITS

In some experiments, it is advantageous to split up each variate into so many subunits in accordance with a second series of treatments—Series *B*—representing subsidiary components of each of the variates of Series *A*. The statistical technique has got to be modified if an accurate appreciation of the effect of all the different treatment factors and of their reaction on one another is to be obtained.

Example 9.—As a test of the influence of the crop on the insect population of the soil, three soil types representing fallow, pasture, and orchard land were examined. Five soil samples were selected at random from each, taken to the laboratory, and a census of the insect population made (Berwick's data).

TABLE 17.—INSECT POPULATION IN SOIL

Soil	Insect order	Sample no.					Total
		1	2	3	4	5	
Fallow	Coccidae...................	1	2	1	1	1	6
	Ants.......................	1	2	1	0	2	6
	Thysanoptera..............	2	3	0	1	1	7
	Other insects, unclassified....	4	3	1	2	1	11
	Total...................	*8*	*10*	*3*	*4*	*5*	*30 (fallow)*
Pasture	Coccidae...................	1	2	1	0	1	5
	Ants.......................	4	3	7	4	30	48
	Thysanoptera..............	17	54	25	27	37	160
	Unclassified...............	20	13	15	23	39	110
	Total...................	*42*	*72*	*48*	*54*	*107*	*323 (pasture)*
Orchard	Coccidae...................	16	23	33	33	27	132
	Ants.......................	56	16	28	16	8	124
	Thysanoptera..............	2	4	2	5	4	17
	Unclassified...............	10	10	1	11	12	44
	Total...................	*84*	*53*	*64*	*65*	*51*	*317 (orchard)*

Insect order total

Coccidae................................ 143
Ants..................................... 178
Thysanoptera............................ 184
Unclassified............................. 165
Grand total............................ 670

In the compilation of these data, a count was first made of the total number of insects in each of the 15 soil samples. The 15 values obtained in this way were then each split into 4 by classifying the insects observed under 4 insect orders. This subdivision gave a total of 60 subunits or final variates for statistical analysis. It should be obvious, however, that as originally only 15 soil samples were taken, the maximum number of degrees of freedom for the comparison of the effect of soil type on the insect population considered as a whole cannot exceed 14. The division of the original whole units to subunits in accordance with the tally for each insect order represented does not increase the number of replicates available for the original whole-unit treatment comparisons. Two estimates of the error variance have therefore to be calculated.   The first applies to the whole-unit treatment factors, and is based on the dispersion shown by the original or whole units.   The second applies to the final treatment classes to which the original variates have been subdivided and represents the dispersion of the subunits after due allowance has been made for all the measurable factors affecting the data.   In the complete analysis of variance, the total sum of squares for the 60 final variates has therefore to be apportioned to the following components:

Whole-unit S.S. comprising $\begin{cases} \text{Soil-type S.S.} \\ \text{S.S. within similar samples, } i.e., \text{ the} \\ \quad \text{error S.S. for the whole-unit treat-} \\ \quad \text{ment comparisons} \end{cases}$

Insect order S.S
Interaction: Insect order $\times$ soil type
Error S.S. for the subunit treatment comparisons

In calculating these components, the variable-squared method has been used, and the respective sums of squares have been expressed in *subunit values* throughout.

$$\text{C.F.} = \frac{670^2}{60} = 7,481.7$$

Total S.S. = S.S. of 60 subunit values − C.F.
$$= 1^2 + 2^2 + 1^2 + \cdots 10^2 + 1^2 + 11^2 + 12^2 - \text{C.F.}$$
$$= 11,070.3 \text{ with 59 degrees of freedom}$$

Whole-unit S.S.—There were originally 15 soil samples or whole units.   The required sum of squares is a measure of the total dispersion shown by these 15 values.

Whole-unit S.S. =
$$\frac{8^2 + 10^2 + 3^2 + 4^2 + \cdots 53^2 + 64^2 + 65^2 + 51^2}{4} - \text{C.F.}$$
$$= 3,672.8 \text{ with 14 degrees of freedom}$$

The division of the sum of the squared values by four is necessary, as we are working in subunit values throughout and each of the whole units represents the total of four subunits.

This whole-unit sum of squares represents the combined effect on the insect population of differences between the soil types and the unavoidable differences in the samples from the same soil. These two components have next to be calculated.

Proceeding now to the other treatment comparisons, the insect-order variance is less than that of error (*b*) and obviously nonsignificant. The calculated value of *z* for the interaction is 1.1877 which compares with a theoretical value at the 5 per cent point of approximately 0.44. This proves that the interaction is significant and the *t* test may be used to compare the treatment totals from which the interaction variance was calculated. The required totals are for each insect order in each soil type.

Insect order	Soil		
	Fallow	Pasture	Orchard
Coccidae................................	6	5	132
Ants....................................	6	48	124
Thysanoptera............................	7	160	17
Unclassified............................	11	110	44

Each of these values represents the total of five subunits so that the standard error of the difference between any pair is $\sqrt{72.9 \times 5 \times 2} = 27.0$. The number of degrees of freedom of the error (*b*) variance is 36, and the value of *t* for a probability of 0.05 is approximately 2. A difference greater than 2×27.0 or 54 is significant. In summarizing the results from such an interaction table, it is best to consider the individual rows or individual columns of values in turn. From the columns, it is obvious that there is no difference in the numbers of each order in the fallow land, but there is a predominance of Thysanoptera and unclassified insects in the pasture land and of Coccidae and ants in the orchard soils. Comparison of values in the individual rows leads to the same conclusion.

To the novice, this type of statistical analysis may appear somewhat complicated. It is, however, merely a logical extension of the technique that would have been used had no subdivision to insect orders been possible. For example, if we ignore this subdivision, the analysis becomes the simple one in which the total sum of squares of 15 variates is split up between the treatment and error components, as follows:

$$\text{Total S.S.} = 8^2 + 10^2 + 3^2 + \cdots 64^2 + 65^2 + 51^2 - \frac{670^2}{15}$$

$$= 14{,}691.2 \text{ with 14 degrees of freedom}$$

Treatment S.S. $= \dfrac{30^2 + 323^2 + 317^2}{5} - \dfrac{670^2}{15}$

$\qquad\qquad$ = 11,216.8 with 2 degrees of freedom

Error S.S. = 14,691.2 − 11,216.8

$\qquad\qquad$ = 3,474.4 with 12 degrees of freedom

The sums of squares and the corresponding variances are exactly four times those quoted in the original analysis of variance for the whole-unit, soil, and error (*a*) components, respectively. The reason for this is that the values quoted above are expressed in whole units, while those in Table 18 are in subunits, each equivalent to one-quarter of a whole unit. The *z* and *t* tests applied to either table would give the same result.

For example, using the second analysis, a significant difference between the totals for each soil would be one greater than

$\sqrt{\dfrac{3,474.4}{12}} \times 5 \times 2 \times 2.179 = 117.1$ (as originally calculated).

Thus the evaluation of the error (*a*) variance is an exact parallel of the simple analysis cited above with the various components quoted in smaller units.

A COMPLEX EXPERIMENT

Table 19 records the daily increment in diameter of two genera of thread blight Marasmius and Corticium of which three isolations of the former and two of the latter are under observation.* Six plates of each isolation were prepared and daily growth measurements were taken over a 3-day period. It is desired to use these data to compare the growth rates of the two genera over the different days and ascertain also whether the various isolations are different fungi or merely separate cultures of one and the same fungus.

It will be seen that, in this experiment, the final treatment units are 15 in number as represented by the totals of each series of six plates recorded at the bottom of each column in the first half of Table 19. Therefore, the treatments account for 14 degrees of freedom. As there are 90 observations in all, the total sum of squares has 89 degrees of freedom and there are 89 − 14 or 75 degrees of freedom available for the estimate of error. More directly, with 15 treatments and six replicates of each, the

* *Trop. Agr.*, 11: 62.

TABLE 19.—DAILY INCREMENTS OF THREAD BLIGHTS IN HALF-MILLIMETER UNITS

Plate	Marasmius isolations									Corticium isolations					
	M_2			M_3			M_4			C_2			C_5		
	1st day	2d day	3d day	1st day	2d day	3d day	1st day	2d day	3d day	1st day	2d day	3d day	1st day	2d day	3d day
1	13	9	15	13	11	9	17	21	14	30	27	23	23	26	25
2	13	14	11	10	10	10	20	20	21	26	27	25	26	30	26
3	15	7	13	13	9	11	26	18	20	25	25	27	19	26	24
4	15	15	14	10	16	11	20	16	15	30	18	35	23	26	24
5	13	17	10	5	8	6	18	16	20	26	26	26	23	31	26
6	12	15	12	12	11	11	24	20	20	28	23	26	26	28	22
Treatment totals.....	81	77	75	63	65	58	125	111	110	165	146	162	140	167	147

Day	Daily totals			Isolation totals	
	Marasmius	Corticium	Total for both genera	Marasmius	Corticium
1st.....................	269	305	574	$M_2 = 233$	$C_2 = 473$
2d.....................	253	313	566	$M_3 = 186$	$C_5 = 454$
3d.....................	243	309	552	$M_4 = 346$	
	765	927	1,692	765	927

within-series or error sum of squares will have $15(6 - 1)$ or 75 degrees of freedom. The basic analysis is therefore:

$$\text{Total S.S.} = 13^2 + 9^2 + 15^2 + \cdots 26^2 + 28^2 + 22^2 - \frac{1,692^2}{90}$$
$$= 4,364.4$$

$$\text{Treatment S.S.} = \frac{81^2 + 77^2 + 75^2 + \cdots 140^2 + 167^2 + 147^2}{6}$$
$$- \frac{1,692^2}{90} = 3,790.7$$

Error S.S. $= 4,364.4 - 3,790.7 = 573.7$

The next step is to split up the treatment sum of squares into its correct components. In assessing these, it is necessary to take into account the fact that the 3-day period is common to all the 15 series and that there may be an interaction between the time factor and the different isolations or genera. The isolations for each genus are entirely independent of one another; consequently there can be no interaction between genus and isolation. The allocation of the 14 degrees of freedom available for treatment will be as follows:

Genus....................................	1
Days.....................................	2
Isolation: Marasmius......................	2
Corticium........................	1
Interactions: Day × genus..................	2
Day × isolations in Marasmius..	4
Day × isolations in Corticium..	2
Total....................................	14

In calculating the respective sums of squares, the variable-squared method has been used throughout. A slight complication is introduced in these calculations by reason of the different number of observations in the various treatment totals. In evaluating certain sums of squares, this complication makes it necessary to divide, in turn, the square of each treatment total by the number of variates it represents, then to sum the resultant values, and to subtract the correction factor.

Factor   S.S.

$$\text{Genus} = \frac{765^2}{54} + \frac{927^2}{36} - \frac{1{,}692^2}{90} = 2{,}898.1$$

$$\text{Day} = \frac{574^2 + 566^2 + 552^2}{30} - \frac{1{,}692^2}{90} = 8.3$$

$$\text{Marasmius isolation} = \frac{233^2 + 186^2 + 346^2}{18} - \frac{765^2}{54} = 751.4$$

$$\text{Corticium isolation} = \frac{473^2 + 454^2}{18} - \frac{927^2}{36} = 10.1$$

Interaction: Day × Genus.—In this calculation, the aggregate treatment effect for these two factors has got to be assessed from the totals of each genus on each day. The interaction is this aggregate sum of squares less the components already calculated for the day and the genus factors independently.

Aggregate day $\times$ genus S.S. =
$$\frac{269^2 + 253^2 + 243^2}{18} + \frac{305^2 + 313^2 + 309^2}{12} - \frac{1,692^2}{90}$$
$$= 2,920$$
$$\text{Interaction} = 2,920 - (\text{S.S. genus} + \text{S.S. day})$$
$$= 2,920 - (2,898.1 + 8.3) = 13.6$$

Interaction: Day $\times$ Marasmius Isolation.

Aggregate S.S. (Day $\times$ Marasmius isolation totals) =
$$\frac{81^2 + 77^2 + 75^2 + 63^2 + 65^2 + 58^2 + 125^2 + 111^2 + 110^2}{6} - \frac{765^2}{54}$$
$$= 782.3$$

Day—for Marasmius alone $= \dfrac{269^2 + 253^2 + 243^2}{18} - \dfrac{765^2}{54} = 19.1$

Marasmius isolation = 751.4 (as already calculated)
Interaction $= 782.3 - (751.4 + 19.1) = 11.8$

Interaction: Day $\times$ Corticium Isolation.

Aggregate S.S. $= \dfrac{165^2 + 146^2 + 162^2 + 140^2 + 167^2 + 147^2}{6} - \dfrac{927^2}{36}$
$$= 110.3$$

Day—for Corticium alone $= \dfrac{305^2 + 313^2 + 309^2}{12} - \dfrac{927^2}{36} = 2.8$

Corticium isolation = 10.1 (as already calculated)
Interaction $= 110.3 - (2.8 + 10.1) = 97.4$

TABLE 20.—ANALYSIS OF VARIANCE

Factor	S.S.	Degrees of freedom	Variance
Total.........................	4,364.4	89	
Treatment:			
Genus.......................	2,898.1	1	2,898.1*
Day.........................	8.3	2	4.1
Marasmius isolation...........	751.4	2	375.7*
Corticium isolation...........	10.1	1	10.1
Interactions:			
Day $\times$ Genus..............	13.6	2	6.8
Day $\times$ Marasmius isolation..	11.8	4	2.9
Day $\times$ Corticium isolation...	97.4	2	48.7*
	3,790.7	14	
Error........................	573.7	75	7.6

* Variances which are significantly greater than the error variance as tested by the F test.

Summary of Results.—The rate of growth of Corticium is distinctly greater than that of Marasmius, the corresponding mean values being 10.6 and 7.1 millimeters, respectively.

The low variance for the time factor indicates that on the average the growth rate remained constant over the 3-day period.

There is a marked difference in the growth rate of the three Marasmius isolations, the mean values being

$$M_2 = 6.47 \text{ mm.}$$
$$M_3 = 5.17 \text{ mm.}$$
$$M_4 = 9.17 \text{ mm.}$$

The standard error of the difference between these means

$$= \sqrt{\frac{7.6 \times 2}{18}} \text{ half-mm.}$$
$$= 0.46 \text{ mm.}$$

As the error variance is based on 75 degrees of freedom, a difference greater than two times the standard error of the difference, *i.e.*, $2 \times 0.46 = 0.92$ millimeter is significant. Thus all three isolations must be regarded as different fungi.

As the interaction Corticium isolation $\times$ day is significant, it is necessary to compare the daily totals of the C_2 and C_5 isolations. These totals are:

	1st day	2d day	3d day
Isolation (half-mm.):			
C_2................................	165	146	162
C_5................................	140	167	147

A difference between these values greater than

$$2 \times \sqrt{7.6 \times 6 \times 2} \text{ or } 19.1 \text{ half-millimeters is significant.}$$

For the 3-day period, there is no difference in the rate of growth of isolation C_2 but C_5 shows a definite increase in increment on the second day. Furthermore, C_5 has grown more slowly than C_2 on the first day but more rapidly on the second day. The significant differences are only just significant at the 5 per cent point, and further experimentation would be required before it

$$\left(\frac{2.064 \times 1.414 \times 6}{5}\right)^2 = 12.26$$

Thirteen replicates might therefore be taken as a reasonable estimate of the number required for the specified level of precision for future experiments. It is only an estimate, as the accuracy of the test depends on the accuracy with which the coefficient of variation can be predetermined from previous research. Also, any marked change in the number of replicates will mean that the value of t used is not strictly correct for the proposed new experiment. If it can be safely assumed that the number of degrees of freedom of the error variance will exceed 30, the equation can be considerably simplified by using a value of t equal to 2.0. The equation then resolves into

$$n = \frac{8\sigma^2}{D^2}$$

On this basis, for the numerical example cited, the number of replicates required would be $\frac{8 \times 6^2}{5^2} = 11.52$. The result agrees sufficiently closely with that already obtained from substitution in the more elaborate formula.

Actually, it is possible by the application of these principles to compile tables from which—provided an estimate of the amount of dispersion likely to be shown by any particular variables is available—the number of replicates of each treatment required for any specified level of precision can be read off. Such tables can be very helpful in drawing up experimental plans, and one of the type suggested by Bird and Gutteridge* has been given in the Appendix (Table VII). For any estimated coefficient of variability, this table records the minimum number of replicates of each treatment series which would be necessary to prove that any stipulated percentage difference between the treatment means is significant. The table is compiled for a value of $P = 0.05$, *i.e.*, for the 5 per cent level of significance. Different values of the coefficient of variability are tabulated along the top of the table, and the treatment differences, expressed as percentages of the mean treatment value, are entered down the left-hand side. For the numerical

---

* *Sci. Agr.*, 14: 5488.

example already cited, reference to the table shows that, for a 6 per cent coefficient of variability, 13 replicates of each series will be necessary if a 5 per cent difference between treatment means is to be significant. This was the number of replicates already obtained by calculation from the original formula. The table may also be used in the reverse direction. In an experiment in which a 9 per cent coefficient of variability is expected and eight replicates of each treatment have been included, only differences between treatment means of 10 per cent or more will be significant.

It is necessary to emphasize that the table has been compiled from values of *t* applicable to data limited to only two treatment series. If it is consulted in connection with experiments involving more than two treatment series, it is therefore subject to the limitations of accuracy already mentioned in connection with the original formula. In these circumstances, the recorded values will be only approximately correct, but the table will still serve as a rough guide in the designing of experiments intended to attain any particular level of precision.

Discussion of experimental precision would not be complete without some mention of the advantages of comprehensive or relatively complex experiments, properly designed so as to permit of a valid analysis of variance of the data. The most obvious advantage is that, in large-scale research, the number of degrees of freedom associated with the error variance is high and, in consequence, the estimate of the standard deviation obtained from the data has a much better chance of approximating to the true value for the whole population. Secondly, a complex experiment including several treatment series in all combinations greatly widens the field of information that would be covered by a number of simple experiments in which each treatment series was tested independently. Experimental results are considerably influenced by environmental factors. For example, storage problems are affected by changes in temperature, livestock development by maintenance conditions, social problems by race and climate, and so on. In simple experiments including only a single series of treatments, all the other influential agencies have got to be standardized as far as possible. The standards used are of necessity predetermined on a somewhat arbitrary basis. By superimposing several distinct series of treatments in a single balanced experiment, it is possible to ascertain, not only the best treatment in each series, but the particular combination of factors which leads to the optimum result. The analysis of variance technique makes it possible to work up the resultant data on an accurate statistical basis. In most research there is an almost endless series of combinations of treatments that might be included in each experiment. It is obvious that the observations have to be limited to a number which can be effectively controlled. The amount of complexity advisable will depend largely on the experience of the staff in charge and on the facilities available for taking the records and carrying out the statistical interpretation of results. In conclusion, therefore, it is advisable to stress the danger of overambitious experimentation. Complex experiments do definitely widen the field of information, but only when they are effectively designed and executed.

USEFUL FORMULAS IN ANALYSIS OF VARIANCE

Let y = any variate.

p = the number of treatments or series.

n = the number of variates in any one series, *i.e.,* the number of replicates.

M = the general mean for all the np variates.

M_t = any treatment mean.

By Direct Calculation.

Total S.S. = $\Sigma(y - M)^2$ with $np - 1$ degrees of freedom

Treatment S.S. = $\Sigma(M_t - M)^2 \times n$ with $p - 1$ degrees of freedom

Error S.S. = total S.S. − treatment S.S. with $p(n - 1)$ degrees of freedom

By Variable-squared Method.

Let T_t = any treatment total.

$$\text{C.F.} = \frac{(\Sigma y)^2}{np}$$

Total S.S. = $\Sigma y^2 - \text{C.F.}$ with $np - 1$ degrees of freedom

Treatment S.S. = $\dfrac{\Sigma T t_t^2}{n} - \text{C.F.}$ with $p - 1$ degrees of freedom

Error S.S. = total S.S. − treatment S.S. with $p(n - 1)$ degrees of freedom

If the assumed-mean method is used, the same formulas apply provided the symbols are taken to represent corresponding values on the table of differences from the assumed mean.

Interactions.—When the treatments are complex in character and include two distinct series of factors A and B, there will be $p_A \times p_B$ possible treatment combinations or treatment types. The treatment sum of squares should be split up into its several components.

Let T_t = the total of the variates belonging to any one treatment type.

T_A = the total of the variates belonging to any treatment in Series A, irrespective of the B factor.

T_B = the total of the variates belonging to any treatment in Series B, irrespective of the A factor.

$$\text{C.F.} = \frac{\Sigma y^2}{n \times p_A \times p_B}$$

Aggregate treatment S.S. $= \dfrac{\Sigma T_t^2}{n} - \text{C.F. with } p_A p_B - 1 \text{ degrees}$
of freedom

Main effects
$$\begin{cases}
\text{Treatment } A \quad \text{S.S.} = \dfrac{\Sigma T_A^2}{np_B} - \text{C.F. with } p_A - 1 \text{ degrees} \\
\qquad\qquad\qquad\qquad\qquad\qquad\qquad\quad \text{of freedom} \\
\text{Treatment } B \quad \text{S.S.} = \dfrac{\Sigma T_B^2}{np_A} - \text{C.F. with } p_B - 1 \text{ degrees}
\end{cases}$$
of freedom

Interaction S.S. = aggregate treatment S.S. − (treatment A S.S. + treatment B S.S.) with $(p_A - 1)$ $(p_B - 1)$ degrees of freedom

Subunits.—When each of the variates in one series of treatments—Series A—can be split up into so many subunits in accordance with a second series of treatments—Series B—two estimates of the error variance should be calculated. One of these estimates can be applied to test the Series A group of treatments and the second the Series B group.

Let Y = any integral variate in Series A, *i.e.*, any whole unit.

y = any subunit value to which the Y variates can be subdivided.

p_A = the number of treatments in Series A.

n = the number of whole units in each of these treatments, *i.e.*, the number of replicates.

p_B = the number of treatments in Series B, *i.e.*, the number of subunits to which each whole unit or Y is divided.

$$\text{C.F.} = \frac{(\Sigma Y)^2}{n \times p_A \times p_B} \quad \text{or} \quad \frac{(\Sigma y)^2}{n \times p_A \times p_B}$$

I. Total S.S. $= \Sigma y^2 - \text{C.F.}$ with $n \times p_A \times p_B - 1$ degrees of freedom

II. Total whole-unit S.S. $= \dfrac{\Sigma Y^2}{p_B} - \text{C.F.}$ with $n \times p_A - 1$ degrees of freedom

II(a). Series A, treatment S.S. $= \dfrac{\Sigma T_A^2}{n \times p_B} - \text{C.F.}$ with $p_A - 1$ degrees of freedom

Error (a) S.S. $= [\text{II} - \text{II}(a)]$ with $p_A(n - 1)$ degrees of freedom

III. Series B, treatment S.S. $= \dfrac{\Sigma T_B^2}{n \times p_A} - \text{C.F.}$ with $p_B - 1$ degrees of freedom

IV. Interaction: series $A \times B = \dfrac{\Sigma T_i^2}{n} - \text{C.F.} - [\text{II}(a) + \text{III}]$ with $(p_A - 1)(p_B - 1)$ degrees of freedom

Error (b) S.S. $= \text{I} - (\text{II} + \text{III} + \text{IV})$ with $p_A(n - 1)(p_B - 1)$ degrees of freedom

Significance.—In an analysis of variance, any component variance is significantly different from the error variance when F, the ratio of the larger variance to the smaller variance, is greater than the reading from the Table of F (Appendix, Table VI) for $P = 0.05$. The reading required is the one for values of n_1 and n_2 on the table equivalent to the number of degrees of freedom of the larger and the smaller variances, respectively. Alternatively, the component variances are significantly different when the difference between $\frac{1}{2} \log_e$ of the individual variances is greater than the reading from the 5 per cent Table of z (Appendix, Table III) for the appropriate values of n_1 and n_2. The t test and the estimated standard errors, as a method of determining significant differences between treatment means or treatment totals, may be validly used only when the F or the z test, applied to the relative treatment variances, has given a significant result.

CHAPTER III

GOODNESS OF FIT AND CONTINGENCY TABLES

The Chi-squared (χ^2) Test

Discussion in the preceding chapters has been limited to problems in which information regarding one or more populations is obtained by means of selecting representative samples from which appropriate measurements are taken. These observations are then used to provide estimates of certain statistics, which make it possible to distinguish between real and fortuitous differences in the data on some predetermined level of probability. There is another type of problem which frequently crops up in scientific research and that is the one in which the observer commences with a certain hypothesis based on some general law of nature or evolved by inductive reasoning. The experimental data in this case are collected in order to test whether the particular material under observation comes within the jurisdiction of the general law, or whether the preconceived hypothesis is in agreement with the actual facts as recorded in the experiment. It is not practicable to take an infinite number of variates and once again the observed data represent merely a sample of the whole and, in consequence, these observed values will not normally tally exactly with the theoretical or expected ones that may be deduced from the original hypothesis. The question that at once arises is, "What are the limits which the deviation between observed and expected values must not exceed if it is to be regarded as caused by errors of random sampling and not by some fundamental discrepancy between the hypothesis and the facts?" The *chi-squared* (χ^2) *test* is the one applied to determine the goodness of fit between the observed and the expected values

$$\chi^2 = \sum \left(\frac{x^2}{m} \right)$$

where x = the difference between the observed and expected values in any one class.

m = the expected value in any one class.

Σ = "the sum of" for all available classes.

Any estimate of χ^2 is therefore based on the magnitude of the difference between the observed and expected values in each class and on the number of classes or independent comparisons available. This latter factor measures the number of degrees of freedom which can be correctly attributed to the estimate of χ^2. The theoretical distribution of χ^2 has been worked out, and this can be used, on much the same principle as that described in connection with the normal distribution, to determine the probability of exceeding any calculated level of χ^2 purely as a result of the ordinary errors of random sampling. Knowing the theoretical distribution, statisticians have been able to compile tables from which this probability can be readily determined. For any particular number of degrees of freedom n, the larger the estimate of χ^2, the greater is the discrepancy between the observed and the expected values and the smaller are the chances that the hypothesis from which the expected values have been determined is correct. It is customary to accept a probability less than 0.05 as sufficient proof of a significant discrepancy between the hypothesis and the observed facts, and it may be assumed that, for probabilities in excess of this, there is no reason to suspect the truth of the hypothesis. This is, of course, a purely arbitrary standard which will generally, but not infallibly, provide an accurate interpretation of the results.

Fisher's Table of χ^2 (Appendix, Table IV) gives the value of χ^2 for selected probabilities P ranging from 0.99 to 0.01 and for degrees of freedom n from 1 to 30. In using the table, it is of primary importance to compare the calculated value of χ^2 with the table reading corresponding to the correct value of n, the number of degrees of freedom represented by the data. The required reading is that corresponding to n on the table equal to the number of independent ways in which the observed values may be compared with the expected. The χ^2 test is valid only when the individuals sampled are independent and when there is a reasonable number of individuals—say not less than five— in each expected class. Provided these relatively simple restrictions are carefully observed, there is probably less risk of a nonvalid use of the table than in the case of certain other statistical tests subject to the assumption of a normal distribution of the variable concerned.

Consider the following very simple example. If a penny is tossed up a very large number of times, one would anticipate, assuming that the penny is properly balanced, that the number of heads and the number of tails recorded would be approximately the same. A penny was tossed 960 times and 516 heads appeared. Is this in agreement with the hypothesis that the penny is not biased?

$$\chi^2 = \sum \left(\frac{x^2}{m}\right) = \frac{(516 - 480)^2}{480} + \frac{(444 - 480)^2}{480} = \frac{2(\pm 36)^2}{480} = 5.40$$

The number of degrees of freedom is, of course, only 1, as when the number of heads has been counted, the number of tails is fixed by subtraction from the total throws. Reference to the Table of χ^2 for $n = 1$ shows that χ^2 equal to 5.40 corresponds to a probability lying between 0.05 and 0.02. (Actual readings are 3.841 for $P = 0.05$ and 5.412 for $P = 0.02$.) Applying the accepted standard for a significant discrepancy $(P < 0.05)$, it must therefore be assumed that the hypothesis that the penny is evenly balanced is wrong.

BINOMIAL DISTRIBUTION

The first theoretical distribution to be established by statisticians was the *binomial distribution*. As the name indicates, this distribution is based on the binomial theorem, and before demonstrating its use in statistics, it is possibly advisable to revise very briefly the binomial expansion. The number of combinations of n articles taken k at a time is given by the symbol $_nC_k$, where

$$_nC_k = \frac{n(n - 1)(n - 2)(n - 3) \cdots (n - k + 1)}{1 \times 2 \times 3 \times \cdots k}$$

The binomial formula gives the expansion of expressions of the type $(x + y)^n$, where n is an integer.

$$(x + y)^n = x^n + {}_nC_1 x^{n-1}y + {}_nC_2 x^{n-2}y^2 + {}_nC_3 x^{n-3}y^3 + \cdots$$
$$_nC_{n-1} xy^{n-1} + y^n$$

The $_nC_k$ factors from each term of the expansion are known as the *binomial coefficients*. $_nC_1$ and $_nC_{n-1}$ both reduce to n so that the coefficients in the above expansion are 1, n, $_nC_2$, $_nC_3$, ... n, 1.

Example 10.—As an example of the application of the binomial theorem in statistical work, let us consider the simple case in which six pennies are tossed repeatedly and the number of heads appearing on each occasion is noted. After a reasonable number of trials, it is possible to draw up a frequency table showing the number of times or frequency 0, 1, 2, up to 6 heads were obtained. In 960 trials the following result was recorded:

No. of heads	Frequency
0	6
1	74
2	219
3	290
4	252
5	108
6	11
Total...............	960

Mathematicians have shown that if the probability that an event will happen is p and that it will not happen is q (when $q + p = 1$) and if a random sample n in number is taken sufficiently often, the frequency distribution showing the number of occasions in which the event should appear 0, 1, 2, . . . n times in any one trial is given by the expansion of the binomial $(q + p)^n$. In the example cited, presuming that the coins are properly balanced, there is an equal chance of a head or a tail appearing at each toss, so that p and q are both equal to $\frac{1}{2}$. As six coins are tossed in each trial, n, the sample or trial number, is six. On the hypothesis that there is no bias in the coins, the frequency distribution showing the frequency with which 0, 1, up to 6 heads should appear will be represented by expansion of the binomial

$$(\tfrac{1}{2} + \tfrac{1}{2})^6 = (\tfrac{1}{2})^6 + 6 \times (\tfrac{1}{2})^5 \tfrac{1}{2} + \frac{6.5}{1.2} \times (\tfrac{1}{2})^4 (\tfrac{1}{2})^2 + \cdots$$
$$6 \times \tfrac{1}{2}(\tfrac{1}{2})^5 + (\tfrac{1}{2})^6$$
$$= \tfrac{1}{2}^6 (1 + 6 + 15 + 20 + 15 + 6 + 1)$$

As there are 960 trials in all, the frequency with which 0, 1, 2, . . . 6 heads may be expected can be calculated by dividing 960 in the proportion of the binomial coefficients given in the parentheses. In **Table 21** these expected frequencies are tabulated alongside the observed, and χ^2 has been evaluated in order to test whether there is any significant difference between them.

TABLE 21—THE EVALUATION OF χ^2

No. of heads	Observed frequency	Expected frequency (m)	x		$\dfrac{x^2}{m}$
			−	+	
0	6	15	9		5.41
1	74	90	16		2.84
2	219	225	6		.16
3	290	300	10		.33
4	252	225		27	3.24
5	108	90		18	3.60
6	11	15	4		1.07
	960	960	−45	+45	16.65 = χ^2
				0	

In the calculation of χ^2, seven comparisons between the observed and the expected frequencies are available. By the time the first six frequencies in each column have been entered, the last one is predetermined as the total frequency in each case must add up to 960. This means that the final value of x is also predetermined by the preceding six entries. There are thus only six independent comparisons, and the number of degrees of freedom of χ^2, as calculated, is only six. Reference to the Table of χ^2 opposite $n = 6$ shows that for $\chi^2 = 16.65$, P lies between 0.02 and 0.01. There is therefore a significant discrepancy between the observed and expected values. The most likely explanation of this is that some of the pennies are slightly biased.

In tossing an ordinary die, there is a $1:6$ chance of a six appearing in any one throw. In tossing five dice a number of times, the frequency distribution showing the number of occasions in which six appears 0, 1, 2, . . . 5 times in any one throw should conform to the expansion of the binomial

$$(\tfrac{5}{6} + \tfrac{1}{6})^5 = (\tfrac{5}{6})^5 + 5 \times (\tfrac{5}{6})^4 \tfrac{1}{6} + \frac{5.4}{1.2} \times (\tfrac{5}{6})^3(\tfrac{1}{6})^2 + \cdot \cdot \cdot (\tfrac{1}{6})^5$$

$$= \frac{1}{6^5}(3,125 + 3,125 + 1,250 + 250 + 25 + 1)$$

The sum of the terms within parentheses is 7,776, and the probability of obtaining n successes, *i.e.*, five sixes in any one throw is therefore only $\frac{1}{7,776}$. In contrast to this, the probability of obtaining not more than one six in any throw is

$$\frac{3,125 + 3,125}{7,776} = 0.804,$$

equivalent on the average to four out of every five trials.

The binomial distribution can sometimes be used with advantage to provide statistical evidence of the significance or otherwise of results of an observational nature. If the chances that an event will or will not occur are equal ($p = q = \frac{1}{2}$), then in a large number of trials, n at a time, the number of successes will be distributed in accordance with the binomial expansion

$$\left(\frac{1}{2} + \frac{1}{2}\right)^n = \frac{1}{2^n}\left(1 + n + \frac{n(n-1)}{1.2} + \cdots n + 1\right)$$

In a single trial the probability of obtaining n successes and no failures is $\dfrac{1}{\text{sum of the binomial coefficients}} = \dfrac{1}{2^n}$. Similarly, the probability of obtaining not more than one failure is $\dfrac{1+n}{2^n}$, and in general, the probability of obtaining not more than x failures is the sum of the first $x + 1$ coefficients divided by 2^n.

In a series of storage tests with grapefruit in which half the fruit was wrapped in cellophane, it was noticed that in 16 out of 20 trials the amount of pitting was obviously greater in the case of the unwrapped fruit. Can it be safely assumed that the wrapping of the fruit has been helpful in reducing the intensity of the pitting? If the cellophane has had no effect, in any one test the wrapped and the unwrapped fruit have equal chances of showing a greater degree of pitting purely as a result of the unavoidable errors of random sampling. From the binomial expansion $(\frac{1}{2} + \frac{1}{2})^{20}$, it would appear that the probability of obtaining, purely by chance, a proportion of 16 to 4 in favor of the cellophane is only $\dfrac{1 + 20 + 190 + 1,140 + 4,845}{2^{20}}$ or approximately 0.006. It can therefore be stated that the cellophane has reduced the amount of damage by pitting.

The binomial expansion provides a relatively simple test of certain types of research data. It is particularly useful in problems in which no numerical values are available. The arithmetical work involved is slight, and for this reason it is sometimes used to carry out a rapid statistical examination of bulky records. It is by no means so critical a test as the *t* test, and when the data permit, the *t* test is the better one to apply.

Example 11.—In the following experiment involving 10 plots of maize, half of each plot was sown with seed which had been treated for smut with formalin, and the other half was sown with untreated seed. The results are recorded in Table 22.

TABLE 22.—YIELDS OF MAIZE FROM TREATED AND UNTREATED SEED

Plot	Average weight of grain per half plot, kg.		Difference in weight in same plot $(T - U)$		Square of differences
	Treated (T)	Untreated (U)	+	−	
1	150	144	6		36
2	177	175	2		4
3	163	150	13		169
4	185	175	10		100
5	139	136	3		9
6	149	133	16		256
7	201	206		5	25
8	170	158	12		144
9	135	128	7		49
10	160	161		1	1
			+69	−6	793
			+63		

$$\text{S.S.} = 793 - \frac{63^2}{10}$$

$$= 396.1$$

$$\text{Mean difference} = 6.3 \text{ kg.}$$

$$\text{Standard error of the mean difference} = \sqrt{\frac{396.1}{9 \times 10}} = 2.10$$

$$t = \frac{6.3}{2.10} = 3.0$$

If the yields for the corresponding half plots are compared, it will be noted that in only 2 out of the 10 plots was the weight of the grain smaller in the case of the treated seed. The probability of this occurring purely by chance is $\dfrac{1 + 10 + 45}{2^{10}}$ or 0.055. By the binomial method of analysis, it would appear that the difference in favor of the treated seed is barely significant.

As the actual weights of seed per half plot have been recorded, it is possible to apply the t test to the data. The calculated value of t works out at 3.0, and reference to the Table of t shows that, for 9 degrees of freedom, the probability of exceeding this value purely by chance is less than 0.02, proving that the mean difference in favor of the treated seed is definitely significant. In this example a more critical analysis of the data has resulted from the use of the t test.

CONTINGENCY TABLES

Observations relative to a given population can often be grouped in several alternative ways. It then becomes possible to draw up a contingency table showing the proportionate number found in each of the selected classes and subclasses.

Example 12.—In an orchard of 1,000 trees a record was taken of the number of shaded to unshaded trees and in each of these classes the proportion of high to low yielding trees. The results are appended in a 2 × 2 contingency table.

TABLE 23.—CENSUS OF AN ORCHARD

	Shaded	Unshaded	Total
High yielders..................	350 (a)	205 (b)	555
Low yielders..................	250 (c)	195 (d)	445
Total........................	600	400	1,000

A cursory examination of these figures shows that shade appears to favor an increase in the proportion of high yielding trees. It is possible to use the Table of χ^2 to ascertain whether this apparent difference is purely fortuitous or whether the proportions within each class are actually influenced by the other factors concerned. This has been termed the *test of independence*. In applying this test, it is necessary to calculate the number of trees in each subclass that might be expected on the assumption that the two main factors of shade intensity and yield capacity are entirely independent. This is achieved by dividing the total number of shaded trees—and then of unshaded trees—in the proportion of high to low yielding trees in the orchard. The expected values are therefore:

$$\text{Shaded high yielders} \dots \dots \dots \dots 600 \times \frac{555}{1,000} = 333 \Bigg\}$$
$$\text{Shaded low yielders} \dots \dots \dots \dots 600 \times \frac{445}{1,000} = 267 \Bigg\} \quad 600$$

$$\text{Unshaded high yielders} \dots \dots \dots 400 \times \frac{555}{1,000} = 222 \Bigg\}$$
$$\text{Unshaded low yielders} \dots \dots \dots 400 \times \frac{445}{1,000} = 178 \Bigg\} \quad 400$$

Total. 1,000

Another way of arriving at exactly the same result would be to divide the total of the high yielders and then of the low yielders in the proportion that the shaded and unshaded trees are of the total. It is fairly obvious that, if a single expected value is calculated, the remaining three can be filled in by subtraction from the totals actually recorded in the respective rows and columns. Thus the expected value for shaded light yielders is $600 - 333 = 267$. As a single expected value determines the remainder, the number of degrees of freedom of χ^2 will be unity.

$$\chi^2 = \sum \left(\frac{x^2}{m} \right)$$ where m represents any expected value and x the difference between this and the corresponding observed value.

$$\chi^2 = \frac{17^2}{333} + \frac{17^2}{267} + \frac{17^2}{222} + \frac{17^2}{178} = 4.876$$

Reference to the Table of χ^2 shows that for $n = 1$, the probability of this value of χ^2 being obtained purely by chance lies between 0.05 and 0.02. This proves that the shade has had a definite influence on the proportion of heavy to light yielders. In this particular orchard, shade is apparently beneficial to the trees. It is necessary to emphasize here that χ^2 is not in any way a measure of the amount of the influence of one class on another; it merely shows whether the two classes are independent or not. Thus, if a similar experiment in another orchard had been carried out and the calculated value of χ^2 corresponded to a probability of 0.01, this does not prove that the effect of the shade in the second orchard is more marked than in the first.

If the expected values are not otherwise required, it is possible to calculate χ^2 for a 2 × 2 contingency table directly from the equation

$$\chi^2 = \frac{(ad - bc)^2(a + b + c + d)}{(a + b)(c + d)(a + c)(b + d)}$$

where a, b, c, d, represent the values in the various subclasses as annotated in Table 23. For the last example,

$$\chi^2 = \frac{(350 \times 195 - 205 \times 250)(1,000)}{555 \times 445 \times 600 \times 400} = 4.876$$

Example 13.—In more complex contingency tables, the calculation of χ^2 is a little more involved, but the technique is merely an extension of the principle described for the 2 × 2 table. As an example of this, let it be assumed that in a second orchard the classification of the trees had been extended to include a third grouping according to three degrees of pruning, *viz.*, heavy, light, and unpruned, and the results were as follows:

TABLE 24

Pruning system	High yielders		Low yielders		Total
	Shaded	Unshaded	Shaded	Unshaded	
Heavy..............	140	90	86	84	400
Light..............	76	69	83	72	300
Unpruned..........	74	71	81	74	300
Total............	290	230	250	230	1,000

The expected values are calculated as before by allocating each column total between its three subclasses in proportion to the totals of these subclasses, *i.e.*, in proportion to the row totals.

Thus, in the first column the entries are calculated as follows:

$$m_1 = 290 \times \frac{400}{1,000} = 116$$

$$m_2 = 290 \times \frac{300}{1,000} = 87$$

$$m_3 = 290 \times \frac{300}{1,000} = 87$$

TABLE 25.—CALCULATION OF x^2

Pruning method	High yielders						Low yielders						Total	
	Shaded			Unshaded			Shaded			Unshaded				
	Ob-served	Ex-pected	$\frac{x^2}{m}$	Ob-served	Ex-pected	$\frac{x^2}{m}$	Ob-served	Ex-pected	$\frac{x^2}{m}$	Ob-served	Ex-pected	$\frac{x^2}{m}$	Ob-served or ex-pected	$\frac{x^2}{m}$
Heavy............	140	116	4.97	90	92	0.04	86	100	1.96	84	92	0.70	400	7.67
Light............	76	87	1.39	69	69	0.00	83	75	0.85	72	69	0.13	300	2.37
Unpruned........	74	87	1.95	71	69	0.06	81	75	0.48	74	69	0.36	300	2.85
Total........	290	290	8.31	230	230	0.10	250	250	3.29	230	230	1.19	1,000	12.89

and similarly with the succeeding columns. The entries in the last row and last column can be filled in by subtraction from the column and row totals, respectively, so that the number of degrees of freedom is only 6. In general, if the contingency table is composed of r rows and c columns, the number of degrees of freedom from which χ^2 is determined will be $(r - 1)(c - 1)$. With complex contingency tables, it is advisable to draw up a second table showing the expected values and the share of χ^2 corresponding to each (Table 25).

χ^2 is 12.89, which for 6 degrees of freedom corresponds to a probability less than 0.05 and is therefore significant. Examination of the distribution of the $\dfrac{x^2}{m}$ values shows that the high numbers are located in the first column and particularly in the heavily pruned, high yielding, shaded subclass. This combination of factors has apparently increased the proportion of heavy yielding trees and is presumably the best cultural practice to follow.

PROBLEMS IN GENETICS

Example 14.—The χ^2 distribution is particularly useful in genetical research as a means of testing whether the recorded data are or are not in agreement with some hypothesis generally based on the Mendelian theory. For example, in a cross between ivory and red snapdragons, Bauer obtained the following in the F_2 generation:

TABLE 26

Phenotype	No. of plants	
	Observed	Expected
Red.............................	22	24.25
Pink............................	52	48.50
Ivory...........................	23	24.25
Total........................	97	

It is desired to ascertain whether these figures show that segregation is occurring in the simple Mendelian ratio of $1:2:1$. The expected values have been calculated on this basis.

$$\chi^2 = \frac{2.25^2}{25.25} + \frac{3.50^2}{48.50} + \frac{1.25^2}{24.25} = 0.527$$

There are 2 degrees of freedom, and the Table of χ^2 shows P to lie between 0.80 and 0.70. The hypothesis is therefore in agreement with the recorded facts.

Example 15.—In an experiment with poultry, a cross between a white rose-combed cock with feathered shanks and a black single-combed nonfeathered hen gave the following results in the F_2 generation:

TABLE 27

Phenotype	No. of birds		$\dfrac{x^2}{m}$
	Observed	Expected	
White, rose comb, feathered..........	115	108	0.453
White, single comb, feathered........	38	36	0.111
Black, rose comb, feathered..........	35	36	0.028
White, rose comb, nonfeathered.......	25	36	3.360
White, single comb, nonfeathered.....	16	12	1.333
Black, single comb, feathered........	13	12	0.083
Black, rose comb, nonfeathered.......	10	12	0.333
Black, single comb, nonfeathered.....	4	4	0.000
Total...........................	256	256	5.701 = χ^2

The expected values have again been calculated on the assumption that each of the three characters is segregating on a simple 3:1 ratio. There are 7 degrees of freedom, and P is therefore approximately 0.6. The results prove that the three allelomorphs are inherited independently as unit characters in which rose comb, white color, and feathered shanks are simple dominants to single comb, black color, and nonfeathered shanks.

Example 16.—In another experiment with poultry, a cross between walnut- and single-combed birds gave progeny with four distinct comb phenotypes (Table 28).

It is obvious that there must be more than a single factor difference between walnut and single comb. The observed numbers in each phenotype are approximately equal and this would occur where two factors are involved in a cross between a double heterozygote and its double recessive. χ^2 has been calculated on this basis and corresponds to a probability slightly below 0.05. This proves that the data are not in agreement with the hypothesis, which may be fundamentally wrong or may merely require some modification in order to bring the observed facts in line with the expected. In either case, a more detailed analysis is required.

TABLE 28

Phenotype	Observed no.	Expected no.	x^2
a. Walnut..........................	94	80	196
b. Pea..............................	62	80	324
c. Rose.............................	75	80	25
d. Single...........................	89	80	81
Total........................	320		626

$$\chi^2 = 626 \div 80 = 7.825$$

On the original hypothesis, if P and R represent the pea and rose genes for dominance, and p and r the corresponding recessive genes, the cross should be of the type

$$PpRr \times pprr = PpRr + Pprr + ppRr + pprr$$

Walnut × single   Walnut   Pea   Rose   Single

(in approximately equal numbers)

In this event, the rose and the pea combs are simple dominants to single, and the walnut comb is the result of the double dominant in the germ plasm. On this assumption, it is possible to use the observed data to ascertain how the unit characters are segregating, which is equivalent to apportioning the total χ^2 among its components. The three available comparisons are:

     I. P vs. p

     II. R vs. r

     III. PR and its reciprocal vs. P or R alone

TABLE 29.—ANALYSIS OF χ^2

Class	Type	Observed	Expected	x^2	$\dfrac{x^2}{m}$	χ^2
I	P present	156	160	16	0.10 ⎱	
	P absent	164	160	16	0.10 ⎰	0.200
II	R present	169	160	81	0.506 ⎱	
	R absent	151	160	81	0.506 ⎰	1.012
III	Double dominant or recessive	183	160	529	3.306 ⎱	
	Single dominant	137	160	529	3.306 ⎰	6.612
Total..						7.824

The total value of χ^2 is the equivalent of that originally calculated. There are 3 degrees of freedom in all, one for each of the components. The respective probabilities read from the Table of χ^2 are, approximately:

Class I................................. 0.60
Class II................................ 0.30
Class III............................... 0.01

The pea- and the rose-comb factors are therefore segregating in accordance with expectation, but the third class is not. There is a marked preponderance of the double dominant and double recessive phenotypes. This indicates that the combination of *PR* and *pr* occurs more frequently than *Pr* or *pR* and leads to the conclusion that linkage between the pea- and the rose-comb factors exists.

Example 17.—In a cross between purple-sweet and white-starchy corn, the following proportional frequencies (after East and Hayes) from 11 different plants were noted in the F_2 generation. The expected values have been calculated on the $9:3::3:1$ ratio of a simple dihybrid.

TABLE 30.—DISTRIBUTION OF PHENOTYPES IN THE F_2 GENERATION OF A MAIZE CROSS

Plant no.	Phenotypes								Total observed
	Purple starchy		Purple sweet		White starchy		White sweet		
	Observed	Expected	Observed	Expected	Observed	Expected	Observed	Expected	
1	102	99	32	33	31	33	11	11	176
2	84	81	27	27	25	27	8	9	144
3	99	99	33	33	31	33	13	11	176
4	80	72	21	24	21	24	6	8	128
5	82	81	27	27	24	27	11	9	144
6	81	72	19	24	21	24	7	8	128
7	104	108	42	36	31	36	15	12	192
8	82	81	29	27	25	27	8	9	144
9	84	81	27	27	25	27	8	9	144
10	91	90	35	30	26	30	8	10	160
11	32	45	20	15	19	15	9	5	80
Total.......	921	909	312	303	279	303	104	101	1,616

Similar calculations, applied to the remaining 10 families, provided the full χ^2 analysis of Table 32.

TABLE 32.—DETAILED ANALYSIS OF χ^2

| Family | Components of χ^2 | | | χ^2 for each family |
	I (purple vs. white)	II (starchy vs. sweet)	III	
1	0.121	0.032	0.090	0.243
2	0.334	0.037	0.000	0.371
3	0.000	0.122	0.363	0.485
4	1.042	1.042	0.057	2.141
5	0.037	0.148	0.606	0.791
6	0.668	1.500	0.500	2.668
7	0.111	2.252	0.232	2.595
8	0.334	0.037	0.049	0.420
9	0.334	0.037	0.000	0.371
10	1.200	0.300	0.278	1.778
11	4.267	5.400	0.022	9.689
Total....	8.448	10.907	2.197	21.552

Each of these components utilizes 1 degree of freedom, so that the total χ^2, *i.e.*, 21.552, has 33 degrees of freedom. The Table of χ^2 does not record probabilities for degrees of freedom n exceeding 30. When n is greater than 30, the distribution of $\sqrt{\chi^2}$ is approximately normal, and the x of the normal distribution may be taken as equivalent in numerical value, irrespective of sign, to $\sqrt{2\chi^2} - \sqrt{2n - 1}$. This expression is used to evaluate x from the data, and the probability that χ^2 is insignificant may then be ascertained from the Table of x. The larger the value of n, the number of degrees of freedom of χ^2, the more accurate does this test become. In the last example,

$$\sqrt{2\chi^2} - \sqrt{2n - 1} = \sqrt{2 \times 21.552} - \sqrt{2 \times 33 - 1} = 1.497$$

From the Table of x, $P = 0.14$, approximately, proving that the hypothesis and the data as a whole are in agreement.

The column totals, each having 11 degrees of freedom, show that segregation of the unit characters is occurring according to expectation in the $3:1$ ratio for purple to white and starchy to sweet. The totals for the individual families prove that the first 10 have behaved strictly according to expectation. In the last family, however, the expected 3:1 ratios do not occur, the probability value for this component (9.689) being less than 0.05. This does not upset the general hypothesis. The family in question may have been subjected to some peculiar influence, *e.g.*, insect or fungal attack affecting seed formation. That some abnormality occurred is suggested by the fact that the total number of grains recorded for this plant is very much less than the average for the other 10. Actually, when a critical probability of 0.05 is being used, a single deviation as large as that shown by family 11 is to be expected, at least once, in a frequency array showing the contributions to χ^2 for each degree of freedom out of a total of 33.

Thus, the complete analysis does make it possible to give a more critical interpretation of the data, as it not only takes into consideration the general results but also traces to its source any deviation from normal among the various components from which the total χ^2 is determined.

Another distribution to which the χ^2 test applies is the *Poisson* series. Like the binomial, it is an example of a discrete distribution, in which entries generally occur in the form of integers, and the range of possible values is limited. Therefore, the Poisson series contrasts with the normal distribution which theoretically may include any intermediate value from $-\infty$ to $+\infty$. In research work, the use of the Poisson distribution is limited to certain specialized problems, in which P, the probability of the event occurring, is very small. Its application presupposes the recognition of data which can correctly be classified as belonging to the Poisson series. Yule points out that the advanced student may find this distribution of considerable theoretical interest, but further discussion here would definitely be out of place. This brief explanatory note has been included only because the student will find this distribution discussed in more technical works on statistics.

CHAPTER IV

DIAGRAMS

Before the present regime in which the research worker is expected to give mathematical proof—or its equivalent—of the accuracy of his conclusions, a diagrammatic presentation of the data was one of the chief means used to interpret results. With the recent advances in statistical technique, there has been a tendency to regard the diagram as an obsolete method which mathematical treatment has rendered no longer necessary, whereas, in fact, the two methods are supplementary. Efficient statistics supply adequate evidence that the conclusions are valid and not based merely on apparent differences in the data due entirely to chance variation outside the control of the operator. Diagrams record the data in an easily assimilated form and make it possible to obtain a clear grasp of the facts that the mathematics have proved to be correct. For reference purposes, diagrams are particularly useful, as they demonstrate at a glance the salient features of the results of previous experiments and show up points of resemblance and difference between these and the current year's data. Furthermore, they will often indicate certain features, sometimes of fundamental importance, that have been entirely overlooked in the statistical analysis. Statistical elaboration is only effective where the data are sufficient to yield a competent estimate of the standard deviation. The design of an experiment, especially in new lines of research, may be such that mathematical proof of certain apparent differences is quite impossible. The diagrams should show which of these are likely to be important and guide the research worker in the planning of later experiments so as to obtain sufficient data for a statistical examination of these characters. Treatment effects discovered by means of a diagrammatic presentation of the data should, wherever possible, be supplemented by mathematical proof. When this is forthcoming, the results can be safely regarded as conclusive.

The first essential of a good diagram is lucidity; the important features should stand out boldly, so that, merely by perusal of the caption, the observer can not only comprehend what the diagram purports to represent but also interpret for himself the significant features. In this direction the skillful use of colors can often be very effective, but even with plain black-and-white diagrams, a certain amount of care in delineation will generally suffice to emphasize the required points. The commonest mistake is the inclusion of too many contrasting and possibly interacting factors in a single diagram, which instead of clarifying the issue only leads to confusion. The obvious remedy is to spread the data over two or even three separate diagrams, possibly on a reduced scale. By suitable subdivision of the data over the various diagrams, it is possible to emphasize the particular relations between the various factors that are considered to be of greatest importance.

GRAPHS

The most commonly adopted type of diagram is the graph, which in its simplest form shows the behavior of a given character in relation to two contrasting factors plotted on squared paper along axes at right angles. In such a graph, the choice of a suitable scale for each axis is important, and as a general rule it is advisable to aim at obtaining a curve which is located somewhere in the vicinity of the diagonal between the axes. Any change in slope will tend to be accentuated if this plan is followed. Consider Fig. 2*A* in which the effects of varying the cutting rotation on the yield of herbage over a 12-month period are shown. It is obvious that there is a marked increase in total yield from series *A* to *D*; also that for all four treatments the rate of increment tends to decrease after November or December. In Fig. 2*B*, so many factors have been superimposed that a very critical examination is required before the significant features can be determined. In neither of these diagrams has an attempt been made to level out the variation between individual readings by tracing a smooth curve more or less arbitrarily between the plotted points. Adjacent readings are joined by a straight line. This has the advantage of eliminating the human factor in plotting the final curve, shows the actual values from which it was determined, and may even make it apparent that certain fluctuations are not fortuitous but rather the result of some external agency. A useful alternative to the line graph is the columnar one in which

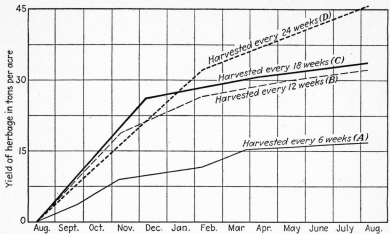

FIG. 2A.—Yields of herbage from four different harvesting rotations, over a period of twelve months.

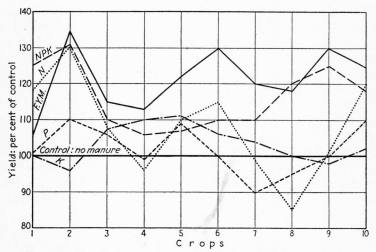

FIG. 2B.—Graph of successive crop yields from different fertilizers.

the recorded values are each represented by an area in the form of a rectangle whose sides are parallel to the axes of the graph. This type of graph is often preferred where the vertical axis shows some quantitative return relative to some time interval as plotted along the horizontal axis. Figure 3*A* is an example in which both methods of presentation have been used effectively. The rainfall is portrayed in the columnar form, the final figure being a histogram. The total rainfall is proportional to the area of the histogram. Comparison of the two graphs shows that on the average an increase in the rainfall coincides with a drop in the dry-matter percentage. This indicates an apparent negative correlation between rainfall and dry-matter percentage. The

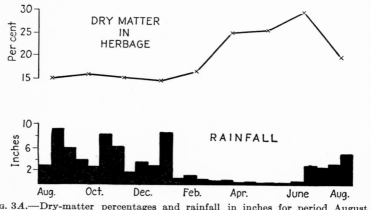

Fig. 3*A.*—Dry-matter percentages and rainfall in inches for period August, 1935, to August, 1936.

dry-matter figures are too few to allow the value of the correlation coefficient to be calculated with any accuracy, and additional records would be required if an estimate of this coefficient was considered essential.

An attempt is sometimes made to demonstrate in a single figure exactly how a given character reacts to changes in three external agencies. With certain types of data, this can be achieved by dividing the columns of the histogram transversely in proportion to the effects of the third factor under consideration. An alternative is to build a solid model of rectangular blocks, so as to depict changes in the interacting factors along three dimensions at right angles. Figure 3*B* shows a model of this type in which the effect of spacing, sowing date, and quantity of fertilizer on the yield of cotton is depicted. It is obvious that the optimum date of sowing lies in August. With early sowing there is little difference in yield as a result of the particular spacing used, but in the later sown plots wide spacing is apparently preferable. The heavier dressings of manure definitely increase yields if applied in July or August but have no advantage over the control if the fertilizer is broadcast too late in the season. This method of presentation is certainly spectacular and effective when the model can be inspected. It has the disadvantage that the figure is rather laborious to construct, and unless the interaction effects are very marked, it is of little use for reproduction in print.

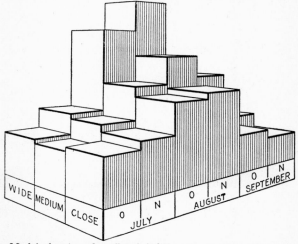

Fig. 3B.—Model showing the effect of different spacings, sowing dates, and nitrogenous fertilizers on the yield of cotton.

GROWTH MEASUREMENTS

In graphs in which growth measurements—weight, height, girth, spread—are plotted against time intervals, there are four alternative methods of presentation. The growth is normally measured along the vertical axis and the time along the horizontal one. The vertical scale may show:

a. The actual measurement.
b. The Napierian logarithm of the measurement ($\log_e$).
c. The increment from the previous measurement.
d. The relative increment from the previous measurement.

The increment c, or more accurately the absolute increment, is assessed by subtraction of the reading at any period from the succeeding one. The rate of increment is estimated by dividing this figure by the number of units of time between the two readings. Where readings are taken at regular intervals, the period between successive readings may be made the unit of time; then the rate of increment is equal to the increment, and the division by the number of time units becomes superfluous. The rate of increment represents the average rate during any particular time interval and should be plotted against the mid-point of this time period on the horizontal scale.

TABLE 33.—MONTHLY WEIGHTS OF A GROWING PIG

Age of pig, weeks	Weight, kg.	Increment, kg.	Rate of increment, kg. per week	Napierian logarithm of weight	Relative increment, % of weight	Relative increment, % per week
4	8			2.0794		
		6	1.5		55.97	13.99
8	14			2.6391		
		8	2.0		45.20	11.30
12	22			3.0911		
		9	2.25		34.29	8.57
16	31			3.4340		
		10	2.5		27.96	6.99
20	41			3.7136		
		10	2.5		21.82	5.45
24	51			3.9318		
		12	3.0		21.13	5.28
28	63			4.1431		
		12	3.0		17.44	4.36
32	75			4.3175		
		13	3.25		15.99	4.00
36	88			4.4774		
		14	3.5		14.76	3.69
40	102			4.6250		

The relative increment takes into account not only the time factor but also the size of the individual for which each increase is recorded. Thus, an increment of 10 feet in the height of a tree originally 20 feet high is obviously less than one of 15 feet in a second tree, but, if the second tree was 50 feet high, its relative increment is actually only about half that of the small tree. The relative increment is measured by the difference between the

Napierian logarithms of successive readings. The difference
between these logarithms, multiplied by 100 and divided by the
number of units of time represented, measures the percentage rate
of increment relative to size at the middle of the period bracketed
by the two readings.

The data from Table 33 recording growth figures of a young pig
over the first 10 months of its life have been used to plot the four
types of graph (Fig. 4A and 4B).

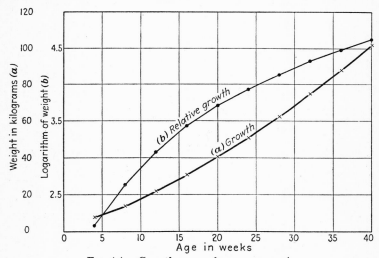

Fɪɢ. 4A.—Growth curves from a young pig.

The first line a obtained by plotting the weight directly against
the age is in the form of an ascending curve indicating that the
older the pig gets the greater is the weight increment in a given
period. Line b is a similar type of graph in which the weight
figures are replaced by their logarithmic values; the slope of this
curve therefore measures changes in relative increments, and in
this example it is apparent that as the pig gets older there is a
fairly steady decline in the rate of increment relative to weight.
The percentage increase in the large pig is distinctly less than in
the small one.

The other two graphs (c and d) are for the absolute and relative
increments, respectively, plotted against the time. These
graphs are rather irregular in character, and it will normally be
found that, where the data are subject to unavoidable variation,

the former two methods of graphical representation will provide a better indication of the nature of the growth.   The increment graphs may add to the information.   For example, in this figure, line *c* appears to be linear in form, proving that the increment is increasing more or less in direct proportion with the age.   The relative increment, however, approximates to a falling curve which is gradually flattening out.   The drop in relative incre-

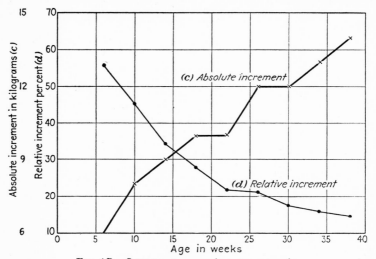

Fig. 4*B*.—Increment curves from a young pig.

ment is much more marked in the first 5 months than in the second.   Assuming that expenses in the form of rations, etc., increase roughly in proportion to the age of the animal, the optimum time to sell would be when this curve of relative increment tends to fall away more steeply for the second time.   This stage has not yet been reached with this particular pig.

FREQUENCY DISTRIBUTIONS

Another diagram of rather a different character is the one obtained by plotting a frequency distribution, of which a simple example has already been given in Fig. 1.   As a more adequate illustration of this type of diagram, the data from Table 34 have been used to plot Fig. 5*A*.   These data represent the frequency distribution of length measurements of 1,000 cacao beans arranged in millimeter classes.

TABLE 34.—FREQUENCY TABLE FOR LENGTH OF CACAO
BEANS IN 1-MM. CLASSES

Length of beans, mm.	No. of beans of each length, frequency
12	0
13	2
14	2
15	3
16	6
17	12
18	37
19	68
20	126
21	171
22	162
23	163
24	110
25	62
26	43
27	23
28	5
29	2
30	2
31	0
32	1
Total....................	1,000

The resultant frequency polygon (Fig. 5*A*) exemplifies many
of the features characteristic of diagrams of this type. The peak
of the polygon, *i.e.*, the class containing the largest number of
individuals is termed the *mode* of the curve. This must be
distinguished from the mean or arithmetic average of all the
readings. In the normal curve which is symmetrical, the
mode and the mean coincide, but the polygon in Fig. 5*A* is

slightly skew and the two ordinates are quite separate, representing values of 21 and 22 millimeters, respectively.

Another very obvious feature of this frequency distribution for cacao beans is that individuals showing extreme deviations from the mean, in either a positive or negative direction, are comparatively rare, but as the class values approach the mean, the number of individuals recorded in each class tends to get progressively greater. Actually, if the number of variates is reasonably large, most curves of this type conform roughly

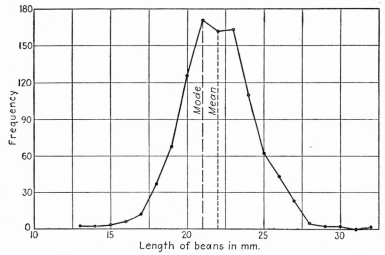

Fig. 5A.—Frequency diagram for length of cacao beans.

to the expansion of the binomial $(a + b)^n$, where a and b are unity and n is the number of classes into which the data have been grouped. When an infinite number of continuous variates are taken and the unit of measurement is made infinitely small, the normal curve, on which many statistical tests of significance depend, will ultimately be reached.

In Table 34, the length of each cacao bean has been recorded to the nearest millimeter. The figures quoted for the length of beans in the first column represent the mean of each class and cover a range of sizes ±0.5 millimeter from the recorded value. Thus, the two beans shown to be 13 millimeters in length may actually measure any length between 12.5 and 13.5 millimeters. This raises the question of the correct allocation of beans whose size is exactly midway between the means of two classes. Should a bean exactly 13.5 millimeters in length be included in the 13 or the 14 millimeter class? Mathematicians stipulate that where this occurs a frequency of one-half should be included in each of the two classes. Provided the method of measurement is sufficiently accurate, the number of individuals showing values exactly midway between classes should be relatively small. Half frequencies may not even appear in the final frequency table, as an even number of half frequencies in any class would make the total frequency of that class an integer.

In Table 34 the length of the beans varies between 13 and 32. In many experiments, the range between the highest and the lowest value is much greater than this, and it may be advisable to reduce the number of classes by making each one cover a wider range of measurements. As an illustration of how this may be done, the data for the length of beans have been grouped below into 7 instead of 21 classes. Each new class includes all values ranging ± 1.5 millimeters from the mean of

TABLE 35.—LENGTH OF CACAO BEANS IN 3-MM. CLASSES

Frequency table				Calculation of the standard deviation		
Class, mm.	Mean of class (m)	Frequency (f)	$f \times m$	Deviation of class mean from general mean $(m - M)$	Frequency $\times$ deviation $f(m - M)$	$f \times (m - M)^2$
				$-$ $\quad$ $+$	$-$ $\quad$ $+$	
12–14	13	4	52	9	36	324
15–17	16	21	336	6	126	756
18–20	19	231	4,389	3	693	2,079
21–23	22	496	10,912	0	0	0
24–26	25	215	5,375	3	645	1,935
27–29	28	30	840	6	180	1,080
30–32	31	3	93	9	27	243
Total..		1,000	21,997		*1701*	6,417

General

$$\text{mean } (M) = \frac{21,997}{1,000}$$
$$= 22.0$$

S.S. $= 6,417$

$$\sigma = \sqrt{\frac{6,417}{999}}$$
$$= 2.53$$

the class.   The *class interval, i.e.,* the difference between the mean
values of successive classes, is now 3 millimeters, or three times
as great as that originally used.   The method in which the
recorded values have been regrouped is also indicated in Table **34**.

The data from this second frequency table have been plotted
in Fig. *5B*.   This illustrates the general rule that coarser group-

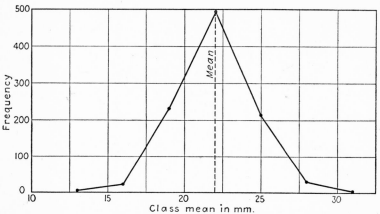

Fɪɢ. *5B.*—Frequency diagram for length of cacao beans arranged in 3-mm.
classes.

ing normally gives a much more regular type of frequency curve,
because the uncontrollable variation between adjacent frequencies tends to be leveled out.   In this graph, the mode and
the mean actually coincide.   There is, of course, a limit beyond
which an increase in the size of the class interval is likely to lead
to a loss in accuracy, especially if it is intended to use the frequency table to calculate the standard deviation of the variates.
In this example, the number of classes has been reduced below
the acceptable minimum; seven readings will rarely suffice to
fix a frequency curve with any accuracy.   If the class interval
is not too large, the loss of accuracy caused by grouping is
negligible.   This rule holds good, provided the class interval
does not exceed one-quarter of the value of the standard deviation.   In this experiment, as we shall see, the class interval is
actually greater than the standard deviation, proving that the
grouping is too coarse.   Statistical calculations based on such a
frequency table would therefore be open to the criticism that an

additional and avoidable grouping error has been added to the estimate of the error variance.

EVALUATION OF STANDARD DEVIATION FROM A FREQUENCY TABLE

Where the data are extensive, the grouping of the variates into a frequency table greatly reduces the routine arithmetic necessary to a statistical analysis. This relatively simple table has been used as a means of demonstrating the various ways in

TABLE 36.—CALCULATION OF STANDARD DEVIATION IN CLASS INTERVALS

Mean of class (m)	Frequency (f)	Deviation in class intervals (d)		$f \times d$	$f \times d^2$
		−	+		
13	4	3		−12	36
16	21	2		−42	84
19	231	1		−231	231
22	496		0	0	0
25	215		1	215	215
28	30		2	60	120
31	3		3	9	27
Total........	1,000	0		569	713

σ (in class intervals) $= \sqrt{\dfrac{713}{999}}$ class intervals $= 0.844$ class interval

$\sigma = 0.844 \times$ class interval

$= 0.844 \times 3$ mm.

$= 2.53$ mm. (as originally calculated)

Similarly, the S.S. $= 713$, in class intervals

$= 713 \times 3^2$ mm.

$= 6,417$ mm. (as originally calculated)

which the standard deviation can be estimated from data arranged in the form of a frequency table. The direct calculation of the sum of squares of the deviations from the mean is shown in the second half of Table 35. In calculating M and σ, it must be remembered that two factors have got to be considered, the mean of each class (m) and the number of individuals in that class (f).

Thus,

$$M = \frac{\Sigma(f \times m)}{n}$$

and

$$\sigma = \sqrt{\frac{\Sigma[f \times (m - M)^2]}{n - 1}}$$

The column recording the deviations of the class means from the general mean $(m - M)$ will always be in arithmetical progression, and this makes it possible to work throughout in class

TABLE 37.—CALCULATION OF STANDARD DEVIATION BY ASSUMED-MEAN AND VARIABLE-SQUARED METHODS

Class mean (m)	Frequency (f)	Assumed mean = 20 mm. (M_a)			Variable squared	
		$(m - M_a)$	$f \times (m - M_a)$	$f \times (m - M_a)^2$	$f \times m$	$f \times m^2$
13	4	− 7	− 28	196	52	676
16	21	− 4	− 84	336	336	5,376
19	231	− 1	−231	231	4,359	83,391
22	496	+ 2	+ 992	1,984	10,912	240,064
25	215	+ 5	+1,075	5,375	5,375	134,375
28	30	+ 8	+ 240	1,920	840	23,520
31	3	+11	+ 33	363	93	2,883
		−12 +26	−343 +2,340			
Total	1,000	+14	+1,997	10,405	21,997	490,285

General mean $(M) = M_a + \dfrac{\Sigma[f \times (m - M_a)]}{n}$

$= 20 + \dfrac{1,997}{1,000}$ mm.

$= 22.0$ mm.

S.S. $= \Sigma[f \times (m - M_a)^2] - \dfrac{\{\Sigma[f \times (m - M_a)]\}^2}{n}$

$= 10,405 - \dfrac{1,997^2}{1,000}$

$= 6,417$

$\sigma = \sqrt{\dfrac{6,417}{999}} = 2.53$

$M = \dfrac{f \times m}{n}$

$= \dfrac{21,997}{1,000}$ mm.

$= 22.0$ mm.

S.S. $= \Sigma(f \times m^2) - \dfrac{\{\Sigma(f \times m)\}^2}{n}$

$= 490,285 - \dfrac{21,997^2}{1,000}$

$= 6,417$ mm.

$\sigma = 2.53$ mm.

intervals instead of in actual units of measurement (Table 36). This is particularly useful when the class interval is not an integer. When the class interval becomes the unit, the deviations will be in the form of a regular sequence of positive or negative numbers, 1, 2, 3, 4, etc., on either side of the mean class with zero deviation.

These deviations in class interval units represent the true deviation divided by the class interval.

It is possible to use either the assumed-mean or the variable-squared method for estimating the standard deviation from a frequency table. The former is probably the best general utility method, as it eliminates the need of calculating $\Sigma(f \times m)$ to estimate the general mean and avoids the rather cumbrous multiplications of the variable-squared system. The application of both methods to the same data is shown in Table 37, and is self-explanatory.

CORRELATION DIAGRAMS

Where several factors are being tested, it is often possible to use the same series of individuals to provide measurements for two or more different characters. These characters may be interdependent to a greater or less extent, an alteration in one tending to produce some corresponding change in the other. In physics and chemistry, the relationship is often so complete that a change in one factor produces an exactly proportionate change in the second. In most biological problems, the affinity is much less evident, but it is possible to obtain some idea of the general nature of the association by plotting a *dot diagram*. In making a dot diagram, the characters are not plotted against changes in some variable external factor such as time intervals, but the values recorded for one character as measured along the abscissa are plotted against the corresponding readings for the second character along an ordinate at right angles. Each plotted point is located by the coordinates of the two characters for one individual. It is therefore essential to keep a record of the individuals to which each particular measurement refers. If a change in one character produces a proportionate change in the second, the plotted points will be in a straight line. If the variation in one character has no influence on the readings recorded for the second, the dots will be scattered irregularly all over the diagram. Depending on the degree of association between the two factors, the arrangement of the dots may be anything between these extremes. Figure 6 has been plotted from the data in Table 38 recording the rainfall and mean yield of maize over a 25-year period. It is very obvious from the scatter of the 25 dots that high yields are on the average associated with seasons of high rainfall. In interpreting such a diagram, it is generally advisable to divide it into four quadrants by drawing the axes intersecting the scales at the mean values of their respective factors. These quadrants have been numbered I to IV in sequence. Practically all the dots lie in the first and third quadrants; this is typical of data in which high values

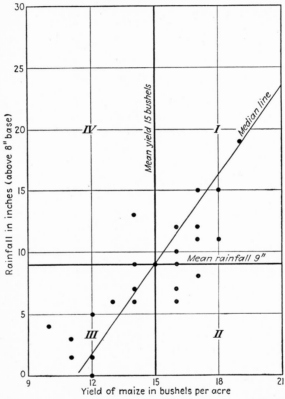

Fig. 6.—Dot diagram for rainfall and yield of maize over a 25-year period.

in the one factor tend to correspond to high values in the second. In other words, there is a *positive* correlation between rainfall and yield. Since the dots cluster fairly closely round the median line as plotted arbitrarily, it can be assumed that the correlation is high and that rainfall and yield are closely linked. An arrangement of dots similar to the above but located in the second and fourth quadrants would indicate the same degree of association between the two factors, but of the opposite sign in which an increase in the values of one character tends to be linked with a decrease in those of the second. Such an arrangement would show a *negative* correlation. If the dots lie more or less evenly in all four quadrants, it can be assumed that there is no correlation between the two characters.

CHAPTER V

CORRELATION

Scientific research generally entails the consideration of a number of interacting factors, and it is often of primary importance to know exactly the extent to which these various factors influence one another. The correlation or degree of association can be measured mathematically by calculating the *correlation coefficient*. In estimating this, a table should be drawn up to show, for any recorded value of one factor, the corresponding value of the second. Table 38 is of this type and records, for each year from 1883 to 1907, the mean yield of maize in Ohio and the corresponding rainfall for the crop season. These data have been used to exemplify the computation of a simple correlation coefficient.

CALCULATION OF A CORRELATION COEFFICIENT

Example 18.—The entries in the last column of Table 38 are obtained by multiplying the deviation for any x variate by the deviation of the corresponding y variate, taking into consideration signs, $+$ or $-$, of these deviations. The total of these product deviations is termed the *sum of products* or *S.P.* Where there are n pairs of readings, the sum of products will have $n - 1$ degrees of freedom. Just as the mean sum of squares is known as the variance, so the sum of products divided by the number of degrees of freedom has been termed the *covariance*. The correlation coefficient r, between the two variables x and y, is given by the expression

$$r = \frac{\text{covariance } xy}{\sqrt{\text{variance } x \times \text{variance } y}}$$

As the readings are in pairs, the number of degrees of freedom of each variance and of the covariance is the same, and therefore

$$r = \frac{\text{S.P.}}{\sqrt{\text{S.S. } x \times \text{S.S. } y}}$$

TABLE 38.—YIELD OF MAIZE, AND NUMBER OF INCHES OF RAIN IN OHIO FROM 1883 TO 1907

Year	Rainfall — Total for season, in. (above base of 8 in.) (x)	Deviation from mean rainfall (d_x)		Deviation^2 $(d_x{}^2)$	Maize — Yield, bu. per acre (y)	Deviation from mean yield (d_y)		Deviation^2 $(d_y{}^2)$	Product deviation $d_x \times d_y$	
		−	+			−	+		−	+
1883	19		10	100	19		4	16		40
1884	11		2	4	18		3	9		6
1885	13		4	16	14	1		1	4	
1886	0	9		81	12	3		9		27
1887	6	3		9	13	2		4		6
1888	3	6		36	11	4		16		24
1889	15		6	36	17		2	4		12
1890	4	5		25	10	5		25		25
1891	5	4		16	12	3		9		12
1892	7	2		4	14	1		1		2
1893	6	3		9	16		1	1	3	
1894	1	8		64	12	3		9		24
1895	1	8		64	11	4		16		32
1896	26		17	289	20		5	25		85
1897	7	2		4	16		1	1	2	
1898	8	1		1	17		2	4	2	
1899	6	3		9	14	1		1		3
1900	9		0	0	14	1		1		0
1901	9		0	0	16		1	1		0
1902	12		3	9	17		2	4		6
1903	12		3	9	16		1	1		3
1904	15		6	36	18		3	9		18
1905	11		2	4	17		2	4		4
1906	10		1	1	16		1	1		1
1907	9		0	0	15		0	0		0
		−54	+54			−28	+28		−11	+330
Total....	225	0		826	375	0		172	+319	

$$\text{Mean rainfall} = \frac{225}{25} = 9 \text{ in.}$$

$$\text{Mean yield} = \frac{375}{25} = 15 \text{ bu.}$$

$$\text{Correlation coefficient } (r) = \frac{+319}{\sqrt{826 \times 172}} = +0.85$$

This is the expression that has been used in calculating r for the data recorded. The value of the correlation coefficient is therefore dependent on the dispersion of the variates within each factor independently and on the extent to which the deviation of any given variate is reproduced in its opposite number.

When a positive correlation exists, positive deviations in x will normally coincide with positive deviations in y, and the sum of products will have a high positive value. In a negative correlation, a positive deviation in x will normally be associated with a negative deviation in y, and vice versa, and the sum of products will have a high negative value. When the variation in the two factors is entirely independent, positive and negative deviations for any pair of variates will occur purely by chance, and on the average of a large number of readings, the product deviations will tend to cancel one another, giving a relatively low figure for the sum of products. The correlation coefficient may take any value between $+1$ and -1. It is not affected by the units in which the variables are measured. If r is zero, the two factors are independent; while the nearer r approaches to ± 1, the greater the degree of correlation. The sign of r will be the same as that of the covariance and determines whether the correlation is positive or negative, *i.e.*, whether an increase in the one factor is associated with an increase or with a decrease in the second.

SIGNIFICANCE OF A CORRELATION COEFFICIENT

Here again, the data used to calculate r represent only a sample of the whole population, and the value of r obtained is therefore only an estimate of the true coefficient of correlation. To ensure even reasonable accuracy in this estimate, a relatively large number of variates are required. It has been demonstrated that for $n = 100$, a value of r of ± 0.3 may be obtained purely by chance from two characters known to be entirely independent. In many experiments, the number of readings available is often of necessity very much fewer than this, and with small samples it is essential to apply a critical test of the significance of the estimated correlation coefficient. In a correlation based on n pairs of variates, the standard error normally attributed to r is either $\dfrac{1 - r^2}{\sqrt{n}}$ or $\dfrac{1 - r^2}{\sqrt{n - 1}}$. Fisher points out that the correlation coefficient may not be normally distributed and that, when the sample is small or the correlation high, this standard error does not provide a fair estimate of significance. With the relatively small samples that in biological research have perforce often to be used to estimate the correlation coefficient, the expression for the standard error has to be modified to

$$\frac{\sqrt{1 - r^2}}{\sqrt{n - 2}}$$

The number of degrees of freedom attributed to r has been reduced to $n - 2$, and the square root of $1 - r^2$ has been introduced. This modified expression is therefore bound to give a higher value than that calculated from the standard formula, and, if used in conjunction with the Table of t, it provides a critical test of the significance of a correlation coefficient evaluated from a limited number of pairs of observations. In this test, the Table of t represents values of the correlation coefficient in terms of the standard error. Thus

$$t \text{ (by calculation)} = \frac{r}{\sqrt{1 - r^2}/\sqrt{n - 2}}$$
$$= \frac{r \times \sqrt{n - 2}}{\sqrt{1 - r^2}}$$

If reference to the Table of t for degrees of freedom equivalent to $n - 2$ shows that this calculated value of t corresponds to a value of P less than 0.05, the correlation coefficient may be considered significant. Applying this test to the data in Table 38, in which the number of pairs of readings is 25,

$$t \text{ (by calculation)} = \frac{0.85 \times \sqrt{23}}{\sqrt{1 - 0.85^2}} = 7.73$$

For 23 degrees of freedom, the Table of t shows that the probability of exceeding this calculated value purely by chance is very much less than 0.01. The reading of t for $n = 23$ and $P = 0.01$ is only 2.87 as compared with the figure of 7.73 computed from the data. This correlation coefficient of $+0.85$ is therefore definitely significant, and it can be safely stated that, in the particular county to which the data refer, high yields of maize coincide with seasons of relatively heavy rainfall.

EASY METHODS OF EVALUATION

The short methods of computation by squaring the variates or the deviations from an assumed mean can generally be used with advantage in calculating the correlation coefficient. The estimation of the sum of squares of x and y presents no new features. By the variable-squared method the sum of products is equal to

$$\Sigma(xy) - \frac{\Sigma x \times \Sigma y}{n}$$

By the assumed-mean system, the same expression holds good if the symbols x and y are taken to represent deviations from their respective assumed means. The application of this system to rather more complex data is shown in the next example.

Example 19. Calculation of r from a Frequency Table by Assumed-mean Method.—Ideally r should be computed from a large number of pairs of observations. Where this is practicable, the arithmetical work can be greatly reduced by grouping the variates into classes in a *correlation table* showing the frequency with which readings for a given class in x are distributed over the various classes of y, and vice versa. Table 39 is a correlation table of this type. The records again show the yield of maize and the rainfall over the same 25-year period. The data in this case have been collected from four new centers, giving a total of 100 pairs of observations. It should be noted that such a correlation table bears a marked resemblance to a dot diagram. In this example, the arrangement of the frequencies over the squares enclosed by the table is certainly not a random one. No entries are located in the areas representing low yields and high rainfall or high yields and low rainfall. Most of the entries lie in a strip running diagonally from the first to the third quadrant, indicating a positive correlation between rainfall and yield of maize. If, on the other hand, the frequencies in a correlation table appear to be scattered indiscriminately over all the squares, it is practically certain that no significant correlation exists, and the estimation of r becomes a work of supererogation. In using the correlation table to form a rough idea of the existence or nonexistence of correlation in the data, it is not only the number of squares that are filled up that must be considered, but also the frequency attributed to each. Where the majority of the higher frequencies show some definite arrangement, a few single frequency entries outside this arrangement are not likely to upset the general trend of results. In this table, correlation is apparently present, and

TABLE 39

Correlation table and calculation of S.S. y

Yield, in sacks (unit classes) (y)	Rainfall, in. (3-in. classes) (x)										Class frequency for y (f_y)	Deviation of class from assumed mean of 13 (d_y)	$f_y \times d_y$	$f_y \times d_y^2$	Sum of individual frequencies in row × deviation from assumed mean of columns $\Sigma(f \times d_x)$	Product deviation from assumed means $d_y \times \Sigma(f \times d_x)$
	2	5	8	11	14	17	20	23	26	29						
20							1				1	+7	+7	49	+9	+63
19									1		1	+6	+6	36	+15	+90
18					1						1	+5	+5	25	+3	+15
17				2		1				1	4	+4	+16	64	+24	+96
16			1								1	+3	+3	9	−3	−9
15				3	1		1				5	+2	+10	20	+12	+24
14			6	10	5						27	+1	+27	27	+6	+6
13		4	7	12	9	3					28	0	0	0		0
12	2		2	4		2					10	−1	−10	10	−12	+12
11		4	8	3	1						15	−2	−30	60	−48	+96
10	1		1	1	1						5	−3	−15	45	−18	+54
9	1										2	−4	−8	32	−9	+36
Class frequency for x (f_x)	4	9	25	35	17	6	2	0	1	1	100		−63 +74	377	−96 +69	−15 +486
													+11		−27	+471

Calculation of S.S. x

	2	5	8	11	14	17	20	23	26	29	
Deviation of class from assumed mean of 11 (d_x)	−9	−6	−3	0	+3	+6	+9	+12	+15	+18	
$f_x \times d_x$	−36	−54	−75	0	+51	+36	+18	0	+15	+18	−165 +138 → −27
$f_x \times d_x^2$	324	324	225	0	153	216	162	0	225	324	1953
Sum of individual frequency in column × deviation from assumed mean of rows $f \times d_y$	−4	−16	−13	+11	+9	+5	0	0	+6	+4	
Product deviation from assumed means $d_x \times \Sigma(f \times d_y)$	+36	+96	+39	0	+27	+30	0	0	+90	+72	+471

(*Explanation is on page 112.*)

the data have been used to estimate r by the assumed-mean method. The calculations are shown in full and should be self-explanatory.

Mean yield (M_y) = assumed mean of $y + \dfrac{\Sigma(f_y \times d_y)}{n} = 13 + \dfrac{11}{100}$

$$= 13.11 \text{ bu.}$$

S.S. $y = \Sigma(f_y \times d_y^2) - \dfrac{[\Sigma(f_y \times d_y)]^2}{n} = 377 = \dfrac{11^2}{100} = 375.8$

Mean rainfall (M_x) = assumed mean of $x + \dfrac{\Sigma(f_x \times d_x)}{n} =$

$$11 + \dfrac{-27}{100} = 10.73 \text{ in.}$$

S.S. $x = \Sigma(f_x \times d_x^2) - \dfrac{[\Sigma(f_x \times d_x)]^2}{n} = 1{,}953 - \dfrac{27^2}{100} = 1{,}945.7$

The final column in the correlation table records the product deviations from the assumed means. To compute the true sum of products based on deviations from the real means of x and y, the total of this column has to be corrected. The correction factor here is

$$\frac{\text{The total deviation of } x \times \text{ the total deviation of } y}{n}\text{ (from their respective assumed means)}$$

This value has got to be subtracted from the total of the last column of the table, taking into account the signs, positive or negative, of the various values.

$$\text{S.P.} = \Sigma[d_y \times \Sigma(f \times d_x)] - \frac{\Sigma(f_y \times d_y) \times \Sigma(f_x \times d_x)}{n}$$

In this example,

$$\text{S.P.} = +471^* - \frac{11 \times -27}{100} = +474.0$$

$$\text{Correlation coefficient } r = \frac{\text{S.P.}}{\sqrt{\text{S.S. } x \times \text{S.S. } y}}$$

$$= \frac{+474}{\sqrt{1{,}945.7 \times 375.8}}$$

$$= +0.55$$

* This value has been calculated from the rows and from the columns independently as a check on the arithmetic.

In this example $n - 2$ equals 98, and the Table of t gives only the theoretical distribution of t for degrees of freedom ranging from 1 to 30. Above this number of degrees of freedom, t approximates to the values given in the Table of x for the normal distribution, and when n is large, the Table of x or the reading from the Table of t for $n = \infty$ may be validly used to test the significance of r.

$$t \text{ (by calculation)} = \frac{+0.55 \times \sqrt{98}}{\sqrt{1 - 0.55^2}}$$
$$= 6.55$$

The Table of t shows this value to be significant on a probability much less than 0.01. With large samples, this test is almost identical with the use of the ordinary standard error of r. The correlation of $+0.55$ is certainly significant proving once again that an increase in the rainfall tends to produce a rise in the mean yield of maize.

STATISTICAL COMPARISON OF CORRELATION COEFFICIENTS

When two or more independent estimates of the coefficient of correlation of a given population are available, it is often of some importance to ascertain whether they are significantly different or not. The distribution of r may not be normal, and the calculated standard errors in conjunction with the Table of t should not be used to determine whether the difference between the individual estimates of r is significant or not. It is possible, however, to express any value of r in terms of z, and as z is known to be distributed normally, the standard tests of significance based on the normal distribution as elaborated in the Table of x may then be validly applied.

$$r \text{ (in terms of } z) = \frac{\log_e (1 + r) - \log_e (1 - r)^*}{2}$$

If n represents the number of pairs of observations from which r has been estimated, the standard error of z is equal to $\dfrac{1}{\sqrt{n - 3}}$.

Significance of Difference between Two Estimates of r.—In the preceding examples, two estimates of the correlation between rainfall and yield of maize have been worked out, *viz.*,

---

* *Cf. z* used in the comparison of two variances (p. 42).

$$r_1 = +0.85 \text{ from 25 pairs of observations}$$
$$r_2 = +0.55 \text{ from 100 pairs of observations}$$

The corresponding z values, as obtained by substitution in the above expression, are

$$z_1 = 1.2561$$
$$z_2 = 0.6184$$
$$\text{Difference} = 0.6377$$

The standard error of this difference $z_1 - z_2$ is from first principles the square root of the sum of the squares of the individual standard errors. n_1 and n_2 are 25 and 100, respectively, and therefore

$$\text{Standard error of the difference } z_1 - z_2 = \sqrt{\frac{1}{22} + \frac{1}{97}}$$
$$= 0.236$$

To be significant, a difference between values that are normally distributed must be greater than twice its standard error. The difference of 0.6377 ± 0.236 is therefore definitely significant. The actual probability can be read from the Table of x:

$$x \text{ (by calculation)} = \frac{0.6377}{0.236} = 2.702$$

Reference to the Table of x shows that this calculated value of 2.702 corresponds to a probability less than 0.01. This proves that the correlation between rainfall and yield of maize tends to be higher in the locality where the first series of records was taken than in the other centers. A possible explanation of this might be deduced from an examination of the major soil types in the difference areas.

Comparison of Several Estimates of r from Same Population.— When a number of independent estimates of any correlation coefficient are available, as computed from different samples from the same apparent population, it is often advantageous to determine the mean value of r for the whole of the recorded data. This not only provides a convenient method of summarizing the results but may also prove satisfactorily the existence of correlation in cases in which one or more of the independent estimates are nonsignificant. The mean coefficient of correlation is obtained by expressing each estimate of r in terms of z, calculating the mean z from these and changing this mean back to the corresponding value of r. This technique is valid only when the total number of correlation coefficients combined together to provide the mean value is small in comparison with the number of variates in the individual samples. Hayes and Garber,[*] from data covering a number of consecutive years, record a positive correlation between the yield of wheat and the size of the individual grains. It is possible to use the data, quoted below, for three separate harvests to calculate the mean value of this correlation coefficient.

Year	No. of selections or samples from which each r was calculated (n)	Correlation coefficient (r)	$\frac{1}{2}[\log_e (1 + r) - \log_e (1 - r)]$
1914	70	+0.431	+0.4611
1915	70	+0.519	+0.5759
1916	70	+0.356	+0.3723
Total.			1.4093

$$z_M - \text{mean value of } z = \frac{1.4093}{3} = +0.4698$$

The corresponding value of r is calculated from

$$r = \frac{e^{2z} - 1}{e^{2z} + 1} = \frac{2.7183^{2z} - 1}{2.7183^{2z} + 1}$$

r may be evaluated directly from the above expression with the aid of ordinary logarithms, but it is simpler to obtain the value of e^{2z} by ascertaining from the table of Napierian logarithms the number whose Napierian logarithm is $2z$. In the above example, $2z = 0.9396$, and reference to the table of Napierian logarithms shows that this is the logarithm of 2.559.

$$r_M, \text{ the mean value of } r = \frac{2.559 - 1}{2.559 + 1} = +0.4380$$

z_M is normally distributed, and its standard error is $\dfrac{1}{\sqrt{p(n - 3)}}$, where p is the number of independent estimates of r, and n the number of individuals in each sample from which these estimates were derived.

[*] "Breeding Crop Plants," McGraw-Hill Book Company, Inc., New York.

The standard error of z_M in the above example $= \dfrac{1}{\sqrt{3(70-3)}}$

$$= \frac{1}{\sqrt{201}} = 0.0705$$

z_M is much greater than twice its standard error and therefore significant, proving that there is a definite positive correlation between the seed size and yield of wheat, with a mean value of r, over a 3-year period, of $+0.4380$.

The transformation of z to r can be simplified if Fisher's Table VB ("Statistical Methods for Research Workers"), showing values of r for different values of z from 0 to 3, is available.

The size of the different samples, from which the various estimates of r have been obtained, is not always the same, and when this occurs, it is necessary in calculating z_M to take into account the number of variates in the samples from which each individual z has been determined.   In these circumstances the best formula to use is

$$z_M = \frac{z_1(n_1 - 3) + z_2(n_2 - 3) + \cdots z_p(n_p - 3)}{n_1 + n_2 \cdots n_p - 3p}$$

where p samples with $n_1, n_2, \ldots n_p$ variates, respectively, are available, giving values of r equivalent to $r_1, r_2, \ldots r_p$ or $z_1, z_2, \ldots z_p$, respectively.   This will ensure that the final estimate of z_M is weighted correctly in accordance with the number of individuals in the various samples from which it has been determined.

The standard error of z_M will be equivalent to

$$\frac{1}{\sqrt{n_1 + n_2 + n_3 + \cdots n_p - 3p}} = \frac{1}{\sqrt{\Sigma n - 3p}}$$

The collection of data for the determination of the correlation coefficient between yield of wheat and size of grain was continued for two more years, and the full data are recorded in Table 40 along with the requisite calculations for the computation of the mean value (r_M) for the 5-year period.

$$\text{Standard error of } z_M = \frac{1}{\sqrt{293}} = 0.0584$$

z_M is much greater than twice its standard error and is therefore significant.

$$e^{2z} = e^{0.8150} = \log_e 2.259$$

$$r_M = \frac{1.259}{3.259} = +0.3863$$

The mean coefficient of correlation is therefore $+0.3863$, a value which is definitely significant. In calculating this mean value, it is assumed that the independent estimates of r, as evaluated annually, all belong to the same general population, and that any differences between them represent the ordinary errors of random

TABLE 40.—VALUES OF r AND z FOR CORRELATION BETWEEN YIELD OF WHEAT AND SIZE OF SEED, 1914–1918

Year	No. in sample (n)	Correlation co-efficients for each year r	Corresponding values of z
1914	70	$+.431$	$+.4611$
1915	70	$+.519$	$+.5759$
1916	70	$+.356$	$+.3723$
1917	35	$+.580$	$+.6624$
1918	63	$+.109$	$+.0620$
Total............	308		

$z_M =$

$$\frac{(0.4611 + 0.5759 + 0.3723)67 + 0.6624 \times 32 + 0.0620 \times 60}{308 - 3 \times 5}$$

$$= \frac{119.41}{293}$$

$$= +0.4075$$

sampling. It may happen that one or more of the estimates show an unexpectedly large deviation from the average value, and it might be interesting to know whether these extreme values of r can be regarded as differing significantly from the other estimates.

The χ^2 Method of Testing Homogeneity of a Group of Correlation Coefficients.—The best index to show the degree of difference between a number of independent estimates of r is

$$\chi^2 = \Sigma[(z - z_M)^2(n - 3)] \text{ for all the samples.}$$

This χ^2 will have $p - 1$ degrees of freedom, where p again represents the number of independent estimates or samples from which z_M has been evaluated.

Reference to the preceding numerical example recording the correlation between yield of wheat and size of seed shows that the correlation coefficient for the year 1918 is much lower than for any of the other years. Does this particular estimate lie outside the range of values covered by the ordinary errors of random sampling?

TABLE 41.—CALCULATION OF χ^2 FROM ESTIMATES OF z RECORDED IN TABLE 40

	Estimates of z	z_M	$z - z_M$	n	$(z - z_M)^2(n - 3)$
z_1	0.4611	0.4705	+0.0563	70	0.212
z_2	0.5759		+0.1684	70	1.900
z_3	0.3723		−0.0352	70	0.083
z_4	0.6624		+0.2549	35	2.078
z_5	0.0620		−0.3455	63	7.162
Total.....					11.435 $= \chi^2$

The Table of χ^2 shows that, for the available 4 degrees of freedom $(p - 1)$, a value of χ^2 of 11.435 corresponds to a probability of approximately 0.02, proving that there is a significant difference between the individual estimates of z.

The standard error of z is $\dfrac{1}{\sqrt{n - 3}}$, so that the standard error of the difference between z_5 and z_1, z_2, or z_3 is $\sqrt{\dfrac{1}{60} + \dfrac{1}{67}} = 0.178$.

A difference between the estimates of z greater than

$$2 \times 0.178 = 0.356 \text{ is significant.}$$

The estimate of r for 1918 is significantly lower than that for any of the other years except 1916. It would appear therefore that in 1918 some factor, possibly some climatic peculiarity, has reduced below normal the degree of correlation usually expected between the yield of wheat and the size of seed.

It should be carefully noted that it is not valid to select one pair of z values out of a group of similar estimates and compare them by means of their standard errors until the χ^2 test has demonstrated that there is a significant difference between the estimates when the group is considered as a whole. The χ^2 test therefore determines whether the population, from which the various samples and estimates of r have been obtained, is homogeneous or not.

PARTIAL CORRELATIONS

The correlation coefficient between two variables A and B measures the extent to which A responds to known changes in B, or vice versa. In any research problem there will usually be other agencies, C, D, E, etc., with which A is also likely to be correlated to a greater or lesser extent. In order to obtain an accurate understanding of the various phenomena at work on the character A, it is not sufficient to base the conclusions on the separate correlation coefficients—AB, AC, AD—calculated independently. The effect of the one agency may be such as to mask or cancel the true influence of the second. For example, heavy rainfall or high summer temperatures may both be positively correlated with high crop yields. It is quite possible, however, for wet seasons to be negatively correlated with temperature, and this would almost certainly lead to an apparent absence of correlation between yield and temperature. Where any character under examination is known to be affected by various external factors, it is essential, in determining any particular correlation, to make due allowance for all the other influential factors covered by the data. This is best effected by calculating what is termed the partial correlation coefficient to distinguish it from the total correlation coefficient based on data from two factors only, as already discussed in the preceding paragraphs. A *partial correlation* measures the correlation between any two variables, A and B, when the remaining factors C, D, E, etc., are kept constant. The elimination of the influence of the balance of the variables is effected in the mathematical calculations. The first step is to work out the total correlation coefficients for all possible combinations of the variables taken in pairs.

Let X_1, X_2, X_3 represent three interacting factors, and r_{12}, r_{13}, r_{23} the respective total correlation coefficients between each pair. Then the partial correlation $r_{12.3}$ between X_1 and X_2, with X_3 held constant, is given by the equation

$$r_{12.3} = \frac{r_{12} - r_{13} \times r_{23}}{\sqrt{(1 - r_{13}^2)(1 - r_{23}^2)}}$$

TABLE 42.—CALCULATION OF PARTIAL CORRELATION COEFFICIENTS

Total correlation r	r^2	$1 - r^2$	$\log\sqrt{1 - r^2}$	Product term in numerator	Numerator	Log numerator	Log denominator	Partial correlation log	Partial correlation Value
$r_{12} = +0.80$	0.64	0.36	$\bar{1}.7781$	+0.224	+0.576	$\bar{1}.7604$	$\bar{1}.8803$	$r_{12.3} = \bar{1}.8801$	+0.759
$r_{13} = -0.40$	0.16	0.84	$\bar{1}.9620$	−0.448	+0.048	$\bar{2}.6812$	$\bar{1}.6964$	$r_{13.2} = \bar{2}.9848$	+0.097
$r_{23} = -0.56$	0.3136	0.6864	$\bar{1}.9183$	−0.320	−0.240	$\bar{1}.3802$	$\bar{1}.7401$	$r_{23.1} = \bar{1}.6401$	−0.436

Example 20. Estimation of a Partial Correlation Coefficient.—Yule records the following data showing the total correlations over a 20-year period between:

1. The yield of hay in hundredweights.
2. The total rainfall in inches.
3. The accumulated spring temperature.

$$r_{12} = +0.80,$$
$$r_{13} = -0.40,$$
$$r_{23} = -0.56$$

It is desired to ascertain from these the true effect of rainfall and of temperature on the yield. In determining the two partial correlations from the equation, it is a good plan to work in logarithms throughout and construct a table of the type appended.

The denominator of the algebraic expression is bound to be positive, so that the sign of the partial correlation will be the same as that of the numerator. The table is otherwise perfectly straightforward and merely details an easy and accurate method whereby the value of the right-hand side of the partial correlation equation can be computed.

The determination of the significance of a partial correlation is similar to the t test used for a total correlation coefficient with the proviso that the number of degrees of freedom from which t is computed must be reduced by a quantity equal to the number of factors that have been eliminated in estimating the partial correlation. In this example, n —the number of readings in each series

—is 20, and only a single character is held constant in each partial correlation. Therefore for $r_{12.3}$,

$$t \text{ (by calculation)} = \frac{0.759 \times \sqrt{20 - 2 - 1}}{\sqrt{1 - 0.759^2}} = 4.802$$

Reference to Table of t opposite 17 degrees of freedom shows that this value of t corresponds to a probability markedly less than 0.01. This partial correlation is definitely significant. A similar test applied to the other two partial correlations $r_{13.2}$ and $r_{23.1}$ shows them to be nonsignificant as determined on a probability of 0.05. $r_{13.2}$, the correlation coefficient between yield and spring temperature with the effect of rainfall eliminated, is obviously negligible. This is rather in contrast to the total correlation coefficient r_{13} for the same two factors, whose value of -0.40 approaches the significant level ($P = 0.07$, approximately). It is even possible that the partial and total correlations are significantly different, and, as a test of this, the transformation of the r values to z has been carried out.

$$r_{13} = -0.40 \qquad z_1 = \frac{\log_e 0.60 - \log_e 1.40}{2} = \overline{1}.5763$$

$$r_{13.2} = +0.097 \qquad z_2 = \frac{\log_e 1.097 - \log_e 0.903}{2} = 0.0974$$

$$\text{Difference, } \overline{z_1 - z_2} = -0.5211$$

The number of degrees of freedom is 18 and 17, respectively, so that the standard error of this difference is $\sqrt{\frac{1}{18} + \frac{1}{17}} = 0.338$. The difference does not exceed twice its standard error and is therefore not significant.

From these results, it becomes obvious that the climatic factor which is of primary importance in influencing yield is the rainfall. This conclusion illustrates another important point in the interpretation of correlations, *viz.*, the need of starting with some logical hypothesis which will make it possible to separate, for any given correlation, the causative attribute from the dependent one. In this example, there is no doubt but that it is the rainfall which is influencing the yield of the crop. With other data in which close affinity can be proved between the attributes, a satisfactory evaluation of the results may be impracticable on account of the impossibility of defining whether it is X that is responsible for changes in Y or vice versa. For example, a positive correlation between root development and number of tillers might mean either that plants with numerous tillers develop a bigger root system or that a good root system encourages tillering. The mechanical computation of correlation coefficients is of little practical value without the necessary knowledge of the basic character of the attributes which alone will lead to a valid interpretation of results. A lack of understanding of this principle has been responsible for some misuse of the correlation weapon in the past, and, in some instances, has led to apparently striking but false deductions. These in turn have tended to attach to the correlation coefficient a certain degree of disrepute which is entirely unwarranted. There can be no doubt that in the hands of the expert, the proper application of the correlation theory has added greatly to scientific knowledge, particularly in sociological and biological problems; also even with the novice, errors of interpretation may be safely avoided if deductions from the correlation coefficients are limited to examples in which the basic premises are known to be accurate.

It is possible to extend the partial correlation equation to cover data in which more than three interacting factors have to be taken into consideration in estimating correlation effects. Take the simplest case in which the data show the corresponding n readings for four variables, and the partial correlation required is that between the first two factors with the last two held constant, *viz.*, $r_{12.34}$. The first step is to calculate, for the four variates taken in pairs, all the total correlations r_{12}, r_{13}, r_{14}, r_{23}, r_{24}, r_{34}. From these, by substitution in the original equation, the three partial correlations $r_{12.4}$, $r_{13.4}$, $r_{23.4}$ can be calculated. These represent the correlations between factors 1, 2, and 3 taken in pairs, when factor 4 has been eliminated. These values can now be used as simple correlations—as designated by the index numbers preceding the point in each r—between three variates 1, 2, 3, in order to assess the partial correlation between 1 and 2, when 3 is held constant.

Thus,

$$r_{12.34} = \frac{r_{12.4} - r_{13.4} \times r_{23.4}}{\sqrt{(1 - r_{13.4}^2)(1 - r_{23.4}^2)}}$$

If, on the other hand, it had been desired to ascertain the correlation between factors 1 and 3, when 2 and 4 are eliminated, the equation then becomes

$$r_{13.24} = \frac{r_{13.4} - r_{12.4} \times r_{23.4}}{\sqrt{(1 - r_{12.4}^2)(1 - r_{23.4}^2)}}$$

The number of degrees of freedom of either of these partial correlations is $n - 2 - 2$ or, in general, where p factors have been eliminated, $n - p - 2$. Tests of significance are exactly as described for total correlations, with the exception of this decrease in the number of degrees of freedom upon which they are based. It will be readily understood that this process of eliminating unwanted factors one by one, in the interpretation of complex data, can be extended theoretically to any number of interacting factors. It is wise, however, to bear in mind that each additional factor will be responsible for a marked and progressive increase in the magnitude of the arithmetical calculations. The following tables have been compiled to facilitate the calculation and interpretation of correlation coefficients:

"Tables of $1 - r^2$ and $\sqrt{1 - r^2}$," by J. R. Miner, Baltimore.

Table VA.—"Values of r for different values of P and n," and Table VB.—"Table of r for values of z from 0 to 3," "Statistical Methods for Research Workers," by R. A. Fisher.

INTRACLASS CORRELATIONS

In the computation of the coefficient of correlation from experimental data, the pairs of readings from which r is determined can usually be correctly allocated to two well-defined classes x and y, *e.g.*, in the correlation between yield and rainfall, parent and child, height and age, etc. If the records are complete, it should not be possible for a variate that rightly belongs to the x group to become included in the y group. With other types of data, it may be impossible to tell from any character difference which reading of any pair belongs to the x and which to the y group. It then becomes immaterial how the allocation of the pairs between x and y is made. Thus in determining the correlation between paired chromosomes in the somatic cell, it might be impossible to differentiate between the individuals in any one pair. Or again, twin ram lambs are obviously identical types, and in measuring the correlation between such twins, no classification to type is practicable.   On the other hand, if one of each pair is a ewe and the other a ram lamb, the observations would naturally be grouped according to sex, x for the female and y for the male.

Example 21.   Computation of Interclass and Intraclass Correlation Coefficients for Twin Lambs.—When the pairs of readings cannot be accurately separated into two distinct x and y classes, the method of calculating the coefficient of correlation is slightly modified to evaluate what is termed the *intraclass correlation* as distinct from the interclass correlation as previously discussed.   As a means of illustrating the difference in procedure, the interclass and the intraclass correlation coefficients have both been worked out for the following data for the weight of twin lambs at 3 months of age.   In the first calculation, the x readings are taken to be for ewe lambs and the y readings for ram lambs, when the interclass correlation is the one required.   In the second calculation, all the twins are assumed to belong to the same sex, when no x and y classification is practicable and the intraclass correlation is the one to apply.

TABLE 43.—CALCULATION OF INTERCLASS CORRELATION COEFFICIENT
FOR TWIN LAMBS OF OPPOSITE SEX

Females (x)				Males (y)				$d_x \times d_y$	
Weight, kg.	Deviation from mean of x (d_x)		d_x^2	Weight, kg.	Deviation from mean of y (d_y)		d_y^2		
	−	+			−	+		−	+
26	3		9	29	2		4		6
33		4	16	32		1	1		4
20	9		81	24	7		49		63
28	1		1	29	2		4		2
24	5		25	28	3		9		15
33		4	16	37		6	36		24
35		6	36	34		3	9		18
32		3	9	33		2	4		6
27	2		4	35		4	16	8	
32		3	9	29	2		4	6	
290	−20	+20	206	310	−16	+16	136	−14	+138
Mean = 29	0			Mean = 31	0				124

Interclass

$$\text{correlation,} \ r_{xy} = \frac{\text{S.P.}}{\sqrt{\text{S.S.} \ x \times \text{S.S.} \ y}} = \frac{+124}{\sqrt{206 \times 136}} = +0.741$$

$$\text{Standard error of} \ r_{xy} = \frac{\sqrt{1 - r_{xy}^2}}{\sqrt{n - 2}} = \frac{\sqrt{1 - 0.741^2}}{\sqrt{10 - 2}} = 0.2375$$

$$t \ (\text{by calculation}) = \frac{0.741}{0.2375} = 3.12$$

For 8 degrees of freedom, this value of t is significant on a probability less than 0.02

In estimating this interclass correlation, the sum of squares of x and the sum of squares of y are calculated separately by squaring the deviations from their respective means. Where no such grouping is practicable, the corresponding x and y readings are interchangeable, and in Table 44, as an indication of this, the first entry of any pair has been designated x' and the second x''. In estimating the intraclass correlation, as the data are nondivisible, the sums of squares and products are based on deviations from the general mean of the whole 20 variates, *i.e.*, of $2n$ variates.

In testing the significance of an intraclass correlation coefficient, it is necessary to transform r to z, using the expression

$$z = \frac{\log_e (1 + r) - \log_e (1 - r)}{2} + \tfrac{1}{2} \log_e \frac{n}{n - 1}$$

With an intraclass correlation, there is an unavoidable negative bias in the estimation of r and a correction has to be applied by adding to z the value of the final term in the equation, *viz.*, $\tfrac{1}{2} \log_e \frac{n}{n - 1}$. For the above example,

$$z = \frac{\log_e 1.63 - \log_e 0.37}{2} + \frac{1}{2} \log_e \frac{10}{9}$$

$$= 0.7940$$

Standard error of z as determined from an intraclass correlation

$$= \sqrt{\frac{1}{n - 3/2}}^{*} = \sqrt{\frac{1}{8.5}} = 0.343$$

* Contrast this with the expression used for estimating the standard error of z for an interclass correlation, *viz.*,

$$\text{Standard error} = \sqrt{\frac{1}{n - 3}}$$

z is normally distributed, so that, to be significant, it must exceed twice its standard error. In this case $r_{x'x''}$ is therefore definitely

TABLE 44.—CALCULATION OF INTRACLASS CORRELATION COEFFICIENT FOR TWIN RAM LAMBS

Weight, kg. (x')	Deviation from general mean $(d_{x'})$		$d_{x'}^2$	Weight, kg. (x'')	Deviation from general mean $(d_{x''})$		$d_{x''}^2$	$d_{x'} \times d_{x''}$	
	−	+			−	+		−	+
26	4		16	29	1		1		4
33		3	9	32		2	4		6
20	10		100	24	6		36		60
28	2		4	29	1		1		2
24	6		36	28	2		4		12
33		3	9	37		7	49		21
35		5	25	34		4	16		20
32		2	4	33		3	9		6
27	3		9	35		5	25	15	
32		2	4	29	1		1	2	
290	−25	+15	216	310	−11	+21	146	−17	+131
								+114	

$$\text{General mean} = \frac{290 + 310}{20} = 30 \text{ kg.}$$

$$\text{Total S.S.} = 216 + 146 = 362$$

$$\text{Intraclass correlation coefficient, } r_{x'x''} = \frac{\text{S.P.} \times 2}{\text{total S.S.}}$$

$$= \frac{+114 \times 2}{362} = +0.63$$

significant, the actual probability as determined from the Table of x being between 0.02 and 0.03

$$\left(x = \frac{0.7940}{0.343} = 2.312 \right)$$

Example 22. Computation of Intraclass Correlation Coefficient for Triplet Lambs.—The estimation of the intraclass correlation need not be limited to examples in which the readings are recorded as n similar pairs. It provides an equally valid method of testing the correlation when the data are arranged in groups of 3, 4, 5, . . . p similar individuals, each group forming, as it were, one family. Suppose, in the last example, that the data recorded had been for triplets and not twins and included the weights for the third member of each family as shown in Table 45. The deviations are again taken from the general mean of the $3n$ readings and the total sum of squares is calculated in the ordinary way. The sum of products is obtained by adding together the product deviations of the three members of each family taken in all combinations two at a time.

TABLE 45.—CALCULATION OF INTRACLASS CORRELATION COEFFICIENT FOR TRIPLET LAMBS

Weight of third lamb, kg. (x''')	Deviation from general mean ($d_{x'''}$) −	+	$d^2_{x'''}$	$d_{x'} \times d_{x''}$ −	+	$d_{x'} \times d_{x'''}$ −	+	$d_{x''} \times d_{x'''}$ −	+
30		0	0		4	0		0	
34		4	16		6		12		8
23	7		49		60		70		42
28	2		4		2		4		2
26	4		16		12		24		8
35		5	25		21		15		35
36		6	36		20		30		24
30		0	0		6	0		0	
32		2	4	15			6		10
26	4		16	2			8		4
300	−17	+17	166	−17	+131	−14	+155	0	+133
					+114		+141		+133

General mean $\dfrac{\Sigma x' + \Sigma x'' + \Sigma x'''}{3n} = \dfrac{290 + 310 + 300}{30} = 30$ kg.

$$\text{Total S.S.} = 216 + 146 + 166 = 528$$
$$\text{S.P.} = +114 + 141 + 133 = +388$$

If p represents the number of members in any family, the intraclass correlation,

$$r = \frac{\text{S.P. for } \frac{p(p-1)}{2} \text{ series of product deviations}}{\text{total S.S.} \times \frac{p-1}{2}}$$

In this example where $p = 3$,

$$r = \frac{\text{S.P. from three series of product deviations}}{\text{total S.S.}}$$

$$= \frac{+388}{528} = +0.7349$$

Where the number in each family (p) exceeds 2, the best estimate of z is obtained from

$$z = \frac{1}{2} \log_e \frac{1 + (p-1)r}{1-r} + \frac{1}{2} \log_e \frac{n}{n-1}$$

When $p = 2$, *i.e.*, when r is a measure of the intraclass correlation for n pairs of similar individuals, this formula reduces to that already given in connection with the data for twin lambs. The same correction for the negative bias in the estimation of r is required. For the above example,

$$z = \frac{1}{2} \log_e \frac{1 + (3-1)0.7349}{1 - 0.7349} + \frac{1}{2} \log_e \frac{10}{9} = 1.1685$$

The standard error of z is, approximately,

$$\sqrt{\frac{p}{2(p-1)(n-2)}}^* = \sqrt{\frac{3}{2 \times 2 \times 8}}$$
$$= 0.306$$

The estimated value of z is much greater than twice its standard error, proving that the correlation of 0.7349 is definitely significant.

Another method of arriving at exactly the same result is to carry out an analysis of variance of the data. The total sum of squares for the $3n$ variates has already been calculated, *viz.*, 528 with 29 degrees of freedom. This total sum of squares can be validly split up into its two components the sum of squares between families and the error of sum of squares, *i.e.*, the sum of

---

* When n is small, this expression does not accurately evaluate the variance of z.

squares within families of three similar individuals. Either of them can be calculated in the usual way, and by subtraction from the total sum of squares, the second component can be assessed.

TABLE 46.—ANALYSIS OF VARIANCE OF DATA FOR TRIPLET RAMS

Factor	S.S.	Degrees of freedom	Variance	$\frac{1}{2} \log_e$ of variance	z
Total...................	528.	29			
Between families..........	434.67	9	48.30	1.9387 ⎫	1.1685
Within families, *i.e.*, error..	93.35	20	4.667	0.7702 ⎬	

This value of z is significant on a probability less than 0.01. The two estimations of z—from the intraclass correlation and from the analysis of variance—are identical. Thus the z test as used in any analysis of variance is essentially a test to find out if the data show any significant correlation between similar individuals, *i.e.*, between members of the same family. If positive correlation exists, the readings for any one family will tend to be similar and, in consequence, the variance within families will be less than that between families; the z test proves whether this difference in variance—in other words, the correlation—is large enough to be considered significant or not. If no correlation is present, the variance within families will be of the same order as that between families. On the other hand, in the case of a negative correlation, a high reading of x' will on the average be associated in the same family with a low reading of x'', and the variance within families will tend to be greater than that between families. The z test can again be used to test whether this difference in variance is significant, *i.e.*, whether the negative correlation is significant.

Unless an estimate of the actual correlation coefficient is required, the analysis of variance is not only the more accurate method of statistical interpretation but is also easier to evaluate, especially for high values of p.

CHAPTER VI

REGRESSION

The regression concept is closely allied to that of correlation in that it is concerned with the way in which changes in one character or variable are reflected or dependent upon simultaneous changes occurring in some other associated variable or variables. The regression function is, however, of wider application than the correlation coefficient and, particularly in biological research, can often be used effectively in problems in which the latter statistic would have little significance. In many correlation problems, the reaction between the associated variables is not mutual in that one factor is the causative agency which produces by any change in value some measurable response in the second factor, the converse being an apparent absurdity. For example, rainfall and yield are often correlated, and this correlation is obviously the result of the influence of the rainfall on the yield and cannot be due to that of yield on rainfall. Yield is then termed the dependent and rainfall the independent factor. In general, if x is the dependent and y the independent factor, the recorded values of x, for any one value of y, will be certain to show the ordinary variation occurring in any random sample taken from that particular population. In other words, the recorded values of x for each value of y will tend to cover a range of readings, say $\pm q$, from their mean. The *regression function* is the one which expresses the *average* value that may be expected from the variates in one factor for any given value of the correlated factor.

If the data were sufficiently extensive, it might be possible to estimate the mean value of x, the dependent variable, for each value of y and to use these means to plot a graph of x against y. With adequate data, this graph will be in the nature of a continuous curve showing how x responds to measured changes in y or, expressed more technically, the *regression of x on y*. The simplest form that the curve can take is a straight line—the line of *linear regression*. This line is accurately defined by the regression equation which may be expressed as

$$X = M_x + b_{xy}(y - M_y)$$

where $X =$ the average value of the x variates that may be
expected when the value of the y variable is fixed
at y.

M_x and $M_y =$ the means of the x and y variables, respectively.

$b_{xy} =$ the *regression coefficient* of x on y, *i.e.*, the number
of units the x variable will change, on the average,
for a unit change in the y variable.

When the reaction between the correlated variables is apparently mutual, *i.e.*, when they cannot be effectively allocated to the dependent and independent classes, the regression of y on x may also be validly computed and may be of considerable statistical significance. This second regression will usually give different values from that of x on y, the equation, in a linear regression, becoming

$$Y = M_y + b_{yx}(x - M_x)$$

where $Y =$ the average value of y for the given value of x.

$b_{yx} =$ the regression coefficient of y on x.

ESTIMATION OF COEFFICIENT OF REGRESSION

Example 23.—In experimental work, the data are seldom complete enough to fix the regression graphs exactly, but they will often suffice to fix a curve which will approximate sufficiently closely to the true one to indicate the general trend of the results.

Table 47 is a correlation table for 100 oat plants in which the number of culms per plant has been recorded against the corresponding yield of grain in grams and the value of the interclass correlation coefficient has been determined. In this example, it is presumed that the dependent factor is the yield x as influenced by the independent factor y, *i.e.*, by the number of culms per plant. In the last three columns of the first half of the table, the average yield of all the plants in each of the six culm classes (2 to 7) has been computed and these figures used to plot Fig. 7A. The plotted points determine, for the recorded data, the location of the regression graph of yield x on number of culms per plant y. There are some obvious irregularities, but the points apparently tend to be located along a straight line—the line of linear regres-

TABLE 47.*—CORRELATION TABLE FOR YIELD OF GRAIN AND NUMBER OF CULMS IN OATS

No. of Culms y	Correlation table — Yield of oats, gm. x								Computation of S.S. y				Product deviations		Data for regression graph x on y		
	1	2	3	4	5	6	7	8	Row frequency (f_y)	Deviation from assumed mean of 4 culms (d_y)	$f_y \times d_y$	$f_y \times d_y^2$	Individual frequencies × deviation from assumed mean of x $\Sigma(f \times d_x)$	Product deviation $d_y \times \Sigma(f \times d_x)$	No. of plants in each culm class, i.e., f_y	Total yield from each culm class, i.e., $\Sigma(f \times x)$	Average yield from each culm class, $\dfrac{\Sigma(f \times x)}{f_y}$
2	1	7	4	1					13	−2	−26	52	−21	+42	13	31	2.39
3		4	17	10	2				33	−1	−33	33	−23	+23	33	109	3.31
4		1	4	15	16	6			42	0	0	0	+22	0	42	190	4.53
5				2	2	3	1		8	+1	+8	8	+11	+11	8	43	5.37
6						1	2		3	+2	+6	12	+5	+10	3	17	5.67
7								1	1	+3	+3	9	+4	+12	1	8	8.00
Column frequency, f_x	1	12	25	28	21	11	11	1	100		−42	114		+98	100	398	

* After Love and Leighty.

TABLE 47.*—(Continued)

	Computation of S.S. x								
Deviation from assumed mean yield of 4 gm. (d_x)	-3	-2	-1	0	$+1$	$+2$	$+3$	$+4$	
$f_x \times d_x$	-3	-24	-25	0	$+21$	$+22$	$+3$	$+4$	$\left.\begin{matrix}-52\\+50\end{matrix}\right\}-2$
$f_x \times d_x^2$	9	48	25	0	21	44	9	16	172

	Product deviations								
Individual frequencies × deviation from assumed mean of y $\Sigma(f \times d_y)$	-2	-18	-25	-10	$+2$	$+7$	$+1$	$+3$	
Product deviation $d_x \times \Sigma(f \times d_y)$	$+6$	$+36$	$+25$	0	$+2$	$+14$	$+3$	$+12$	$+98$

	Data for regression graph y on x								
No. of plants in each yield class, *i.e.*, f_x	1	12	25	28	21	11	1	1	100
Total no. of culms in each yield class, $\Sigma(f \times y)$	2	30	75	102	86	51	5	7	358
Average no. of culms per plant for each yield class, $\dfrac{\Sigma(f \times y)}{f_x}$	2.0	2.5	3.0	3.64	4.1	4.64	5.0	7.0	

*After Love and Leighty.

$$\text{Mean yield, } M_x = 4 - \tfrac{2}{100} = 3.98$$

$$\text{S.S. } x = 172 - \frac{(-2)^2}{100} = 171.96$$

$$\text{Mean culm no. } M_y = 4 - \tfrac{42}{100} = 3.58$$

$$\text{S.S. } y = 114 - \frac{42^2}{100} = 96.36$$

$$\text{S.P. } xy = +98 - \left(\frac{-42 \times -2}{100}\right)$$

$$= 97.16$$

$$\text{Correlation coefficient } r = \frac{+97.16}{\sqrt{171.96 \times 96.36}} = +0.755$$

(*Explanation continues at foot of page 134.*)

sion—which runs in the median position between the plotted points. If the regression can safely be assumed to be linear, it is possible to calculate a statistic from the original records by means of which the line of best fit to the plotted points can be accurately determined within the limits of the prescribed data. The line of best fit is the one which conforms to the principle of *least squares*, which stipulates that the sum of squares of the deviations of the plotted points from the line must be at a mini-

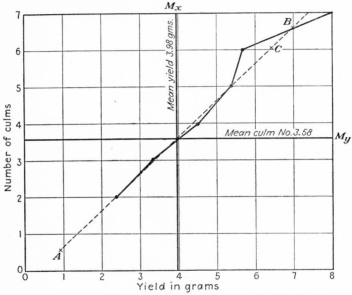

Fɪɢ. 7*A*.—Regression graph of yield of grain in number of culms in oats.

mum. The statistic required to fix this line is the coefficient of regression *b* or, more precisely, where *x* is the dependent and *y* the independent variate, the coefficient of regression of *x* on *y*, *viz.*,

---

Regression coefficient of yield on no. of culms.

$$b_{xy} = \frac{\text{S.P. } xy}{\text{S.S. } y} = \frac{97.16}{96.36} = +1.01$$

Regression coefficient of no. of culms on yield

$$b_{yx} = \frac{\text{S.P. } xy}{\text{S.S. } x} = \frac{+97.16}{171.96} = +0.57$$

$$b_{xy} = r \times \frac{\sigma_x}{\sigma_y} = \frac{\text{S.P. } xy}{\text{S.S. } y}$$

The regression coefficient of yield on number of culms

$$b_{xy} = \frac{\text{S.P. } xy}{\text{S.S. } y} = \frac{+97.16}{96.36} = +1.01$$

This indicates that a deviation of +1 from the mean number of culms is equivalent, on the *average*, to a deviation of +1.01 grams from the mean yield; or, expressed in the form of an equation,

$$d_x = 1.01d_y$$

where d_y represents any given deviation from the mean culm number and d_x the corresponding deviation from the mean yield that might be expected on the average of a large number of readings.

By entering the vertical and horizontal axes M_x and M_y intersecting in the point fixed by the coordinates of the means of x and y, it is possible to use this equation to locate accurately the line of best fit to the plotted points, *i.e.*, the regression line of x on y. In fixing this line, the coordinates of the points corresponding to deviations of +3 and −3 from the mean culm number have been worked out from the equation, making the corresponding average deviations from the mean yield

$$\pm 3 \times 1.01 = \pm 3.03$$

These are the coordinates of the points A and B in the diagram. Therefore, within the limits of the recorded data, the straight line AB represents the linear regression of yield on culm number. It can therefore be used to determine what the average yield of grain is likely to be for any fixed number of culms per plant. It is probably better to work in the absolute units in which the variates are measured instead of in deviations from the means. As

$$d_x = b_{xy} \times d_y$$

then, by substitution, using the annotation given earlier in this chapter,

$$(X - M_x) = b_{xy}(y - M_y)$$

and

$$X = M_x + b_{xy}(y - M_y)$$

Thus, the general equation already given for the regression function is again derived. For the calculated values for the regression of yield on number of culms (Table 47),

$$X = 3.98 + 1.01(y - 3.58)$$
$$= 1.01y + 0.36$$

Thus, if the number of culms y is known to be six, the average yield that may be expected is

$$1.01 \times 6 + 0.36 = 6.42 \text{ gm.}$$

These values represent the coordinates of the point C on the regression graph (Fig. 7A).

Mathematically, the same data may be used to calculate the regression of culm number on yield, *i.e.*, of y on x. This has actually been done, and the regression is again apparently linear (Fig. 7B) with a regression coefficient $b_{yx} = +0.57$. The equations for this second regression function are

$$d_y = b_{yx} \times d_x$$

or, in absolute values of the variates,

$$Y = M_y + b_{yx}(x - M_x)$$

where Y represents the average number of culms for any fixed yield. Theoretically, for any given yield x, the average culm number should be

$$3.58 + 0.57(x - 3.98) = 0.57x + 1.31$$

It is obvious from the nature of the data that the yield of grain cannot determine in any way the number of culms developed by the plant, and therefore these mathematical expressions have no real meaning when applied to this particular problem. This effectively illustrates the futility of applying statistical formulas more or less indiscriminately to any data. Some basic knowledge of the fundamental character of the various attributes under examination is essential to an accurate interpretation of results. In the application of the regression theory, it is important to distinguish between the dependent and independent variates or to know to what extent they are mutually responsive.

The various facts discussed in Example 23 illustrate some general truths applicable to linear regressions. The coefficient of regression is the tangent of the angle that the regression line makes with the appropriate x or y axis of the graph, depending on whether the x or the y variable is the independent factor. For any two complementary regression lines, the line with the smaller

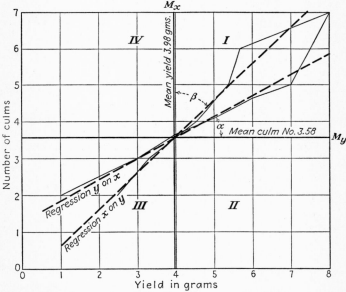

Fig. 7*B*.—Regression graphs; yield of grain on number of culms in oats and number of culms on yield of grain in oats.

inclination to the x axis has x as the independent variable, and b_{yx} is the tangent of the angle that this line makes with the x axis. Similarly, the line with the smaller inclination to the y axis has y as the independent variable, and b_{xy} represents the slope of this line to the y axis. Thus in Fig. 7*B*,

$$b_{yx} = \tan \alpha$$
$$b_{xy} = \tan \beta$$

For any one pair of variables, at least one and possibly both coefficients of regression will be less than unity. They will have the same sign, both positive or both negative, the sign being the same as that of the covariance.   If the graph on which the regression lines are plotted is divided into four quadrants by axes intersecting at a point whose coordinates are the means of the two variables, the regression lines in a positive correlation will be located in quadrants I and III and in a negative correlation in quadrants II and IV.   The more closely the regression lines approach one another, *i.e.*, the more acute the angle between them, the closer is the correlation between the variables, until, at a correlation coefficient of ± 1, the two lines coincide.   In contrast to this, when r is in the region of zero, the regression lines intersect at approximately 90 degrees.   They will always cross at the intersection of the axes through the means M_x and M_y.   In Fig. 7*B* the angle between the regression lines is acute, indicating fairly high correlation; the graphs lie in the first and third quadrants, and the correlation should be positive, its actual value by calculation being $+0.755$.

SIGNIFICANCE OF REGRESSION FUNCTION

In addition to defining the relationship between two variables, the application of the regression function to certain types of research data will often amplify the resultant conclusions by demonstrating any progressive change occurring in the data or by producing a valid reduction of the error variance.   For example, in experiments with crops that are repeatedly ratooned, such as semiperennial pasture or fodder crops, there will often be a tendency for the yields from successive harvests to show a gradual decline.   This may be a result of the senescence factor in the plant or of a gradual reduction in soil fertility or of both. The significance of any such general trend in the variates can be effectively assessed by means of the regression function.

Example 24.   Use of Regression Function in Interpretation of Results.—Table 48 records the yields obtained from an experiment with a fodder crop of guinea grass in which the grass was harvested once per month over an 8-month period.   Do these figures indicate any significant drop in yield from the first to the last crop?   In this experiment, it is the time factor or age of the ratoon that is thought to be affecting the yields, and the regression of yield, x, on age, y, provides an effective test of any significant downward trend in the yield data.

TABLE 48.—YIELD DATA FOR GUINEA GRASS RATOON CROPS

Monthly yields of guinea grass herbage, kg. per $\frac{1}{40}$ acre (x)	Age of crop, months (y)	x^2	y^2	xy
85	1	7,225	1	85
73	2	5,329	4	146
65	3	4,225	9	195
41	4	1,681	16	164
20	5	400	25	100
36	6	1,296	36	216
16	7	256	49	112
24	8	576	64	192
Total...... 360	36	20,988	204	1,210
Mean....... 45	4.5			

$$\text{S.S. } x = 20,988 - \frac{360^2}{8} = 4,788$$

$$\text{S.S. } y = 204 - \frac{36^2}{8} = 42$$

$$\text{S.P. } xy = 1,210 - \frac{360 \times 36}{8} = -410$$

$$b_{xy} = \frac{-410}{42} = -9.762$$

It now becomes necessary to test whether this regression coefficient is significant or not. The sampling variance of b_{xy} is determined from the number of degrees of freedom of the regression coefficient, the sum of squares of the independent variable y, and the sum of squares of the deviations of the plotted points on the regression graph from the line of regression. This last is computed by adding the sum of squares of the deviations of each recorded value of x from its mean value X as determined from the regression equation

$$X = M_x + b_{xy}(y - M_y)$$

The sum of squares required will be

$$\Sigma(x - X)^2$$

As the degrees of freedom of the covariance is $n - 1$ and as the calculation of b uses up 1 additional degree of freedom, $n - 2$

degrees of freedom may be validly allocated to the coefficient of regression.

$$\text{Standard error of } b_{xy} = \sqrt{\frac{\Sigma(x - X)^2}{(n - 2) \times \text{S.S. } y}}$$

In applying this expression to the data for the guinea grass, the first step is to work out X for each value of y in order to estimate $\Sigma(x - X)^2$.

From the regression equation,

$$X = 45 - 9.762(y - 4.5)$$

and therefore

$$X = 88.93 - 9.76y$$

From this equation Table 49 has been compiled.

TABLE 49.—CALCULATION OF $\Sigma(x - X)^2$ FOR DATA OF TABLE 48

x	y	X	$x - X$		$(x - X)^2$
			−	+	
85	1	79.17		5.83	33.99
73	2	69.41		3.59	12.89
65	3	59.65		5.35	28.62
41	4	49.89	8.89		79.03
20	5	40.13	20.13		405.22
36	6	30.37		5.63	31.70
16	7	20.61	4.61		21.25
24	8	10.85		13.15	172.92
				$\Sigma(x - X)^2 =$	785.62

A quicker method of arriving at the same result is to substitute the appropriate values in the identity,

$$\Sigma(x - X)^2 = \text{S.S. } x - b_{xy}^2 \times \text{S.S. } y$$

Therefore, $\Sigma(x - X)^2 = 4{,}788 - (-9.762)^2 \times 42$
$$= 4{,}788 - 4{,}002.4 = 785.6 \text{ (as calculated above)}$$

It is important to note that, in using this short method, b is not only squared but is also multiplied by the sum of squares of y which may be a relatively large number. Therefore, to ensure accuracy, the value of b must be taken to several places of decimals. As an alternative, the equation can be expressed in another form as follows: b_{xy} is assessed from $\dfrac{\text{S.P. } xy}{\text{S.S. } y}$ so that S.S. $x - b_{xy}^2 \times$ S.S. y reduces to

$$\text{S.S. } x - \frac{(\text{S.P. } xy)^2}{\text{S.S. } y}$$

and when the necessary sums of squares are available, this last is the simplest equation to use in estimating $\Sigma(x - X)^2$.

$$\text{Standard error of } b_{xy} = \sqrt{\frac{785.6}{6 \times 42}} = 1.765$$

The significance of b_{xy} can now be determined by calculating t.

$$t = \frac{b_{xy}}{\text{standard error of } b_{xy}}$$
$$= \frac{9.762}{1.765} = 5.53$$

Reference to the Table of t opposite $n = 6$ (the degrees of freedom of the regression function) shows that this value of t corresponds to a probability less than 0.01. b_{xy} is therefore highly significant, proving that the later ratoons show a definite falling off in yield.

Short Method of Computing Sum of Squares When Variates Are in Arithmetical Progression.—In Table 48, the variates of the independent factor y form a regular sequence of numbers in arithmetical progression. This is not an uncommon feature of research data from which correlation or regression coefficients are evaluated, and the following simple method of calculating the sum of squares is worth noting as it effectively reduces the amount of routine arithmetic involved:

For any variable y whose n variates are arranged in a regular sequence at equal intervals of i units,

$$\text{S.S. } y = \frac{n(n^2 - 1)}{12} \times i^2$$

Thus for the data of Table 48,

$$\text{S.S. } y = \frac{8(8^2 - 1)}{12} \times 1^2 = 42 \text{ (as originally calculated)}$$

COMPARISON OF INDEPENDENT ESTIMATES OF COEFFICIENT OF REGRESSION

Example 25.—The experiment from which the guinea grass data (Table 48) were extracted also included yields from 10 crops of elephant grass, as recorded in Table 50.

TABLE 50.—YIELDS OF TEN RATOON CROPS OF ELEPHANT GRASS

Monthly yields of elephant grass, kg. per $\frac{1}{40}$ acre. (x)	Age of crop, months (y)	x^2	y^2	xy
55	1	3,025	1	55
52	2	2,704	4	104
40	3	1,600	9	120
36	4	1,296	16	144
54	5	2,916	25	270
22	6	484	36	132
29	7	841	49	203
24	8	576	64	192
18	9	324	81	162
20	10	400	100	200
350	55	14,166	385	1,582

$$\text{S.S. } x = 14{,}166 - \frac{350^2}{10} = 1{,}916$$

$$\text{S.S. } y = 385 - \frac{55^2}{10} = 82.5$$

Alternatively, by the short method,

$$\text{S.S. } y = \frac{10(10^2 - 1)}{12} = 82.5$$

$$\text{S.P. } xy = 1{,}582 - \frac{350 \times 55}{10} = -343$$

$$b_{xy} = \frac{-343}{82.5} = -4.158$$

$$\Sigma(x - X)^2 = 1{,}916 - \frac{343^2}{82.5} = 490$$

$$\text{Standard error of } b_{xy} = \sqrt{\frac{490}{8 \times 82.5}} = 0.861$$

$$t \text{ (by calculation)} = \frac{4.158}{0.861} = 4.836$$

The probability of exceeding this value of t purely by chance is less than 0.01, as determined from the Table of t for $n = 8$. This proves that with the elephant grass also there is a progressive decline in yield with successive crops from the same stools.

The value of the coefficient of regression for the guinea grass yields is more than double that of the elephant grass. For the former variety the yields range from 85 to 15 kilograms, while for the elephant grass the range is only 55 to 18 kilograms. It might be of advantage to ascertain whether or not these data indicate that the rate at which the yields are declining is greater in the case of the guinea grass. To test this, it is necessary to determine whether the difference between the respective regression coefficients is significant or not. The coefficients of regression which it is desired to compare have been estimated from two distinct series of readings, one series for guinea grass and the second for elephant grass. In a simple analysis of variance applied to the yield data x of this fodder grass experiment, the within-series or error variance would be evaluated from the aggregate of the sums of squares computed from each series independently. For the yield data alone,

Error S.S. = 4,788 + 1,916, with 7 + 9 degrees of freedom
= 6,704 with 16 degrees of freedom

Similarly, the whole of the recorded data should be used in calculating the sum of $(x - X)^2$ from which the standard errors of the estimated coefficients of regression will ultimately be computed. Therefore, for this experiment,

$\Sigma(x - X)^2$ = 785.6 + 490.0, with 6 + 8 degrees of freedom
(Guinea (Elephant
grass) grass)
= 1,275.6 with 14 degrees of freedom

The standard error of any coefficient of regression b_{xy} is evaluated from the expression $\sqrt{\dfrac{\Sigma(x - X)^2}{n - 2 \times \text{S.S.} \ y}}$. The best values of $\Sigma(x - X)^2$ and of $n - 2$ to substitute in this formula are the aggregate ones obtained from the whole of the available data, as calculated above. These aggregate values of $\Sigma(x - X)^2$ and of $n - 2$ may be validly used in calculating the standard error for any of the separate coefficients of regressions computed from the data.   In this experiment, there are two estimates of the coefficient of regression, *viz.*,

(*a*) b_{xy} for guinea grass $= -9.762$
(*b*) b_{xy} for elephant grass $= -4.158$
                         Difference, $D = \overline{5.604}$

It is desired to ascertain whether this difference between the two regression coefficients may be regarded as significant or not.   By substituting the appropriate numerical values in the expression for the standard error of a regression coefficient,

(*a*) '   Standard error of $b_{xy} = \sqrt{\dfrac{1{,}275.6}{14 \times 42}} = \sqrt{\dfrac{91.11}{42}}$

(*b*)   Standard error of $b_{xy} = \sqrt{\dfrac{1{,}275.6}{14 \times 82.5}} = \sqrt{\dfrac{91.11}{82.5}}$

From first principles, the standard error of the difference is the root of the sum of the squares of the individual standard errors, and therefore

$$\text{Standard error of } D = \sqrt{\frac{91.11}{42} + \frac{91.11}{82.5}} = 1.809$$

$$t \text{ (by calculation)} = \frac{D}{E_D} = \frac{5.604}{1.809} = 3.097$$

The available number of degrees of freedom of $\Sigma(x - X)^2$ from which t was calculated is 14.   The nearest reading from the Table of t at this level of n is 2.977 for $P = 0.01$, proving that the difference between the regression coefficients is highly significant. This shows that with successive ratoon crops, the yield of the guinea grass is falling away more rapidly than that of the elephant grass.

LINEAR REGRESSION COMPONENT OF VARIATION

When one variable x shows some measurable response to changes in a second variable y, the dispersion of the x variates must represent the combined effect of the variation induced by the independent factor y and the ordinary errors of random sampling occurring in the dependent factor x.   These two components of the total sum of squares of x represent, respectively, the regression of x on y and the deviations from this regression, both of which may be accurately computed. The second component, *i.e.*, the sum of the squares of the deviations from the regression line, is obtained by using b_{xy} to evaluate $\Sigma(x - X)^2$, where X is the expected value of x—as determined from the regression equation—for each recorded value of y. It has already been shown that

$$\Sigma(x - X)^2 = \text{S.S. } x - \frac{(\text{S.P. } xy)^2}{\text{S.S. } y}$$

The number of degrees of freedom of this component of the total S.S. x will be $n - 2$, where n is the number of variates from which the S.S. x was computed. The first component—the regression of x on y—must account for the balance of the total S.S. x and of the total available degrees of freedom $n - 1$.
Therefore

$$\text{S.S. linear regression} = \text{S.S. } x - \left[\text{S.S. } x - \frac{(\text{S.P. } xy)^2}{\text{S.S. } y} \right]$$

$$= \frac{(\text{S.P. } xy)^2}{\text{S.S. } y} = \frac{(\text{S.P.})^2}{\text{S.S. of independent factor}}.$$

$$\text{with } (n - 1) - (n - 2) = 1 \text{ degree of freedom}$$

The following data for the yield x as recorded against the age y of a crop of guinea grass have been extracted from Table 48 to exemplify the practical application of this technique.

> S.S. $x = 4,788$ with 7 degrees of freedom
> S.S. $y = 42$ with 7 degrees of freedom
> S.P. $xy = -410$

In this example, the yield x is the dependent factor; hence the sum of squares of x represents the aggregate of the sums of squares attributable to the linear regression component and the deviations from this regression. The full analysis of the sum of squares of x is appended:

Factor	S.S.	Degrees of freedom	Variance	F
Linear regression....	$\dfrac{(-410)^2}{42} = 4{,}002.4$	1	$4{,}002.4$	
Deviations from regression..........	$4{,}788 - 4{,}002.4 = 785.6$	6	130.9	30.59

The sum of squares of the deviations from regression 785.6 is identical with $\Sigma(x - X)^2$ as already calculated in estimating the standard error of b_{xy} for the guinea grass data.   In fact, the above analysis provides an alternative method of testing the significance of b_{xy}, the coefficient of regression of yield on age.   If b_{xy} is significant, the linear regression variance will be much larger than the unavoidable errors of random sampling as measured by the deviations from this regression.   The F or the z test may be validly used to determine whether the two variances are significantly different, *i.e.*, whether b_{xy} is significant.   Here, $F = 30.59$ as compared with a reading of 13.74 from the Table of F for $n_1 = 1$, $n_2 = 6$, and $P = 0.01$. b_{xy} is therefore significant on a probability much less than 0.01, precisely the same conclusion as was originally obtained by calculating t from the standard error of b_{xy}.   Both tests are bound to give exactly the same result, and in any particular example, the easier one to evaluate should be used in preference.

REDUCTION OF ERROR VARIANCE BY MEANS OF REGRESSION

In agricultural research, complete control of all the external factors likely to have an influence on the recorded data is not generally possible.   When the simultaneous variation occurring in any such external agency can be effectively computed, the linear regression component of the error variance of the dependent factor may be regarded as a fair measure of the influence of the independent factor on the estimate of error.   The variance of the deviations from this regression may then be validly used to determine the significance of differences between treatment means. The data for the fodder crop experiment with guinea and elephant grass (Tables 48, 50) effectively illustrate the advantages of this technique in practice.   Consider first the ordinary analysis of variance of the yield data alone, x, ignoring for the present the age factor.

$$\text{Total S.S.} = 20{,}988 + 14{,}166 - \frac{710^2}{18} = 7{,}148.5, \text{ with } \mathbf{17} \text{ degrees of freedom}$$

$$\text{Variety S.S.} = \frac{360^2}{8} + \frac{350^2}{10} - \frac{710^2}{18} = 444.5, \text{ with } \mathbf{1} \text{ degree of freedom}$$

This enables Table 51 to be compiled.

TABLE 51.—ANALYSIS OF VARIANCE OF YIELD DATA FOR FODDER GRASS
EXPERIMENT (TABLES 48, 50)

Factor	S.S.	Degrees of freedom	Variance	F
Total	7,148.5	17		
Variety	444.5	1	444.5⎱	1.06
Within variety, *i.e.*, error	6,704.0	16	419.0⎰	

The variety variance is obviously not significantly greater than the error variance, which would indicate that there is no significant difference between the mean yields of the guinea grass and the elephant grass. The respective mean values are 45 and 35 kilograms per plot, and the difference between the variety means is therefore approximately 25 per cent of the general mean. It is at first surprising that a mean difference of this magnitude is not significant, but closer inspection of the data shows that the reason is the rapid falling off in the yields with the increasing age of the crop. This in turn is responsible for excessive dispersion of the variates resulting in an unduly large estimate of error and leading to the nonsignificant result quoted above. It is possible to discount the effect of age on the yield data by extracting the linear regression component from the error variance, so as to leave a reduced estimate of error, equivalent to $\Sigma(x - X)^2$, *i.e.*, the sum of the squares of the deviations from regression. In this example, $\Sigma(x - X)^2$ as already evaluated (Example 25) is 1,275.6 with 14 degrees of freedom. The reduced error variance is therefore $\dfrac{1,275.6}{14} = 91.11$. The standard error of the difference between the mean yields of the guinea grass and the elephant grass now becomes

$$\sqrt{\frac{91.11}{8} + \frac{91.11}{10}} = 4.53$$

The mean difference is 10 kilograms so that t by calculation is $\dfrac{10}{4.53} = 2.208$. Reference to the Table of t at the available 14 degrees of freedom of the reduced error variance shows that this value of t corresponds to a probability between 0.05 and 0.02, proving that the guinea grass has given a significantly higher yield than the elephant grass.   Thus, the elimination of the influence of age on the yield data has been effective in reducing considerably the estimate of error.   This can be expected only when the regression is significant, *i.e.*, when the linear regression component of the variance is definitely larger than the deviations from regression.

ANALYSIS OF COVARIANCE

The analysis of covariance is a term used to define the statistical technique by means of which the complete analysis of the simultaneous variation occurring in two or more correlated variables is effected.   It is a more exact, if rather more intricate, method of discounting the influence on research results of changes occurring in some measurable but uncontrollable external factor. In the analysis of covariance, the regression component is extracted, not only from the error variance, but also from all the other component factors of the total analysis of variance. Furthermore, the regression equation is used to provide a revised estimate of the treatment means, adjusted so as to compensate for the variability of the independent factor.   It is proposed to use the same data (Examples 24, 25) to exemplify a simple analysis of covariance.   The first step is to make out a table, of the type given below, showing the sums of squares and the sums of products for the total and for each of the components in the analysis of variance of the dependent factor x and of the independent factor y.   Some of the required sums of squares and sums of products have not been previously worked out, but it is presumed that the student can by now carry out any of these routine calculations for himself from the original data of Tables 48 and 50.   For example, for the age factor y,

$$\text{S.S. variety} = \Sigma \frac{(\text{variety totals})^2}{\text{no. of variates in each total}} - \text{C.F.,} \quad i.e.,$$

$$\frac{\text{Grand total}^2}{n}$$

$$= \frac{36^2}{8} + \frac{55^2}{10} - \frac{91^2}{18}$$

$$= 4.444$$

Total S.P. $= \Sigma xy - \dfrac{\Sigma x \times \Sigma y}{n}$

$\qquad = 1{,}210 + 1{,}582 - \dfrac{710 \times 91}{18}$

$\qquad = -797.44$

In this way, Table 52 showing the full analysis has been compiled.

TABLE 52.—ANALYSIS OF VARIANCE AND COVARIANCE FOR FODDER GRASS
EXPERIMENT RECORDED IN EXAMPLES 24 AND 25

Factor	Degrees of freedom	S.S.		S.P. (xy)	Deviations from regression $\Sigma(x - X)^2$	Degrees of freedom	Reduced variance
		Yield (x)	Age (y)				
Total...	17	7,148.44	128.94	−797.44	2,216.6	16	
Variety.	1	444.44	4.444	− 44.44	0	0	
Error...	16	6,704.0	124.5	−753.0	2,149.7	15	143.3
				Residual $\Sigma(x - X)^2$	66.9	1	66.9

The last three columns in Table 52 require some further explanation. $\Sigma(x - X)^2$ is calculated from the identity

$$\text{S.S. } x - \frac{(\text{S.P. } xy)^2}{\text{S.S. } y}$$

and is evaluated separately for each line, *i.e.*, for each factor in the analysis. It represents the balance of the sum of squares of x for each factor after the regression component for that particular factor has been deducted, the regression component being $\dfrac{(\text{S.P. } xy)^2}{\text{S.S. } x}$. The regression component in each case accounts for 1 degree of freedom, and the number of degrees of freedom of each $\Sigma(x - X)^2$ is therefore one less than that for the corresponding sum of products. It will be noticed that, for the variety factor, the deviations from regression and the number of degrees of freedom are both zero. With only two treatments, this will always be the case, as obviously with two values, the line of best fit is the straight line connecting them, and the deviations from this linear regression will therefore be nil. When there are more than two treatments, the $\Sigma(x - X)^2$ for the treatment or variety component will generally show a numerical value, as it represents the deviations of the treatment means from the line of regression fitted to them.

Before carrying out an analysis of covariance with a view to improving the estimate of error, it is advisable to make sure that the regression coefficient of x on y is significant.   If the regression is nonsignificant, there is not likely to be much advantage in proceeding further with the covariance calculations.   The best value of the coefficient of regression comes from the error line of the table, and in carrying out an analysis of covariance, this line should be calculated first and the significance of b_{xy} tested.   In this example, the appropriate $b_{xy} = \dfrac{-753.0}{124.5} = -6.05$.   Its significance may be determined in the usual way by calculating the standard error, but it is probably simpler here to use the F test to compare the variances of the regression and the deviations from the regression.   The variance attributable to this linear regression is $\dfrac{753^2}{124.5} = 4{,}554.3$; or alternatively $6{,}704 - 2{,}149.7$. F is therefore $\dfrac{4{,}554.3}{143.3} = 31.78$.   The reading from the Table of F for $n_1 = 1$ and $n_2 = 15$ and $P = 0.01$ is only 8.68, proving that b_{xy} is definitely significant.

It will be noticed that, in the analysis of covariance (Table 52) there is a residual $\Sigma(x - X)^2$ to which the single remaining degree of freedom in the penultimate column can be validly allocated.   This residual variance actually is a measure of the difference between the regression coefficients of the variety and error components.   It is this residual variance which has to be compared with the corresponding variance for error by the F or z tests in order to determine whether there is any significant difference between the treatment means of the dependent variable x after they have been adjusted or corrected for age inequalities by means of the regression coefficient b_{xy}.   In this example, the comparable reduced variances are

		F
Error...............................	143.3	2.142
Residual, *i.e.*, difference between regressions	66.9	

For these data, $n_1 = 15$ and $n_2 = 1$, corresponding to a reading from Table of F of approximately 245. The difference between the variances is therefore quite insignificant. It must therefore be assumed that, when the mean yields of the two fodder grasses are equalized for the age factor, there is no significant difference between them.

This conclusion is apparently contrary to that obtained when the actual mean yields were tested by the error variance with the linear regression component deducted. However, both conclusions are logical, and in order to demonstrate why this is so, it is necessary to calculate the values for the variety means corrected for age. If y_t represents the mean age recorded for any given treatment, from the regression relationship of yield on age, the expected corresponding average deviation—from M_x, the general mean of the dependent variable x—will be $b_{xy}(y_t - M_y)$. The values of $b_{xy}(y_t - M_y)$ represent the amounts by which the respective treatment means have to be corrected in order to put them on an equal age basis as determined by regression. The corrected mean yield will be given by

$$x_t - b_{xy}(y_t - M_y)$$

where x_t = any treatment mean of the dependent factor.

b_{xy} = the coefficient of regression from the error line of the analysis of covariance.

y_t = the mean value of the independent factor corresponding to x_t.

M_y = the general mean of y, the independent factor.

The adjusted mean yields for the fodder grass experiment will be:

$$\text{Guinea grass} = 45 - (-6.05)(4.5 - 5.05)$$
$$= 45 - 3.33 = 41.67 \text{ kg.}$$
$$\text{Elephant grass} = 35 - (-6.05)(5.5 - 5.05)$$
$$= 35 + 2.72 = 37.72 \text{ kg.}$$

When the mean variety yields are corrected for the age factor, the difference between them is reduced from the original 10 kilograms to 3.95 kilograms. It is this difference which the F test comparing the residual with the reduced variance in the covariance table has shown to be nonsignificant.

The complete analysis of covariance proves that the apparent superiority of the mean yield of the guinea grass over that of the elephant grass can be largely attributed to the difference in the mean age of the crops recorded. When the mean yields are adjusted to an equal age basis by means of the regression of yield on age, the guinea grass shows no significant increase in yield over the elephant grass. The analysis of covariance has provided an accurate interpretation of data which otherwise might have been responsible for rather erroneous conclusions. This is a very simple example of the covariance technique, but the application of the same principles to more complex data will be found elaborated in Chap. IX in connection with uniformity trials in field experimentation.

TEST FOR LINEARITY OF REGRESSION LINE

In all the preceding examples of the application of the regression principle to experimental data, it has been assumed that the regression is linear. While this is undoubtedly the form most widely applicable in agricultural research, it is by no means the only form that the regression can take, as the line of best fit to the plotted points on the regression graph may be in the nature of some definite curve rather than a straight line. For correct statistical evaluation, it may therefore be important to be able to recognize those occasions in which the linear regression function will not provide an accurate interpretation of the recorded data, and this can be determined by carrying out a relatively simple test of the straightness of the regression line.

In most problems involving the regression function, there will be several values of the dependent factor recorded against each value of the independent factor. The variates of the dependent factor can therefore be grouped in arrays in accordance with the class of the independent factor with which they are associated. The following data have been extracted from Table 47, which is a correlation table for the yield of oats x recorded against the number of culms y. The number of variates in each array is the number of individuals or frequency in each row of the correlation table, *i.e.*, in each culm class.

The total sum of squares of the yield data—S.S. x—is the aggregate of the sums of squares between arrays and within arrays. The sum of squares between arrays can easily be

TABLE 53.—YIELD OF GRAIN AND NUMBER OF CULMS FOR 100 OAT PLANTS

	Data from Table 47			Direct calculation of deviations from regression			
Culm no. or array mean (m_y)	No. of variates in array (frequency) (f)	Total yield of array (T_a)	Mean yield for each array, i.e., $\dfrac{T_a}{f}$ (m_x)	Predicted mean yield for each array (X_a)	$m_x - X_a$	$(m_x - X_a)^2$	$f(m_x - X_a)^2$
2	13	31	2.39	2.38	0.01	0.0001	0.0013
3	33	109	3.31	3.39	−0.08	0.0064	0.2112
4	42	190	4.53	4.40	0.13	0.0169	0.7098
5	8	43	5.37	5.41	−0.04	0.0016	0.0128
6	3	17	5.67	6.42	−0.75	0.5625	1.6875
7	1	8	8.00	7.43	0.57	0.3249	0.3249
Total...	100	398		S.S. Deviations from regression = 2.9475			

S.S. x = 171.96 Mean yield (M_x) = 3.98
S.S. y = 96.36 Mean culm no. (M_y) = 3.58
S.P. xy = 97.16 b_{xy} = +1.01

calculated from the above data, allowance being made for the different number of variates in the separate arrays.

$$\text{S.S. between arrays} = \Sigma\left(\frac{T_a^2}{f}\right) - \frac{\text{grand total}^2}{n}$$
$$= \frac{31^2}{13} + \frac{109^2}{33} + \frac{190^2}{42} + \frac{43^2}{8} + \frac{17^2}{3} + \frac{8^2}{1} - \frac{398^2}{100}$$
$$= 100.92, \text{ having 5 degrees of freedom}$$
$$\text{S.S. within arrays} = 171.96 - 100.92$$
$$i.e., \text{ error} = 71.04, \text{ with } 99 - 5 \text{ degrees of freedom}$$

The sum of squares between arrays is itself a complex component in that it represents the aggregate effect of the regression of yield on the number of culms and the deviations from this regression.

$$\text{S.S. linear regression} = \frac{(\text{S.P. } xy)^2}{\text{S.S. } y}$$
$$= \frac{97.16^2}{96.36} = 97.97, \text{ with 1 degree of freedom}$$

Deviations from regression = 100.92 − 97.97
$$= 2.95, \text{ with 4 degrees of freedom}$$

The within-array variance provides a fair estimate of the uncontrollable sampling errors of the yield data with the influence of the independent factor eliminated. If the regression is truly linear, the variance of the deviations from the regression should not differ significantly from that of error. This may be tested in the usual way, by calculating F or z. The full analysis is appended.

TABLE 54.—ANALYSIS OF VARIANCE OF YIELD DATA x

Factor	S.S.	Degrees of freedom	Variance
Total........................	171.96	99	
Between arrays:			
Linear regression..............	97.97	1	
Deviations from regression.....	2.95	4	0.738
Within arrays or error...........	71.04	94	0.756 $\Big\}$ $F = 1.024$

The variance of the deviations from regression is obviously not significantly different from that of error, proving that it may safely be assumed that the regression of yield on number of culms is linear in form.

The similarity between the covariance technique and this test for the straightness of the regression line is fairly obvious, especially if the arrays are regarded as the equivalent of the treatment or variety grouping of the covariance table. It is possible to calculate the sum of squares of the deviations from regression directly, and this has been done in the second half of Table 53, as it may help the student to a clearer understanding of the exact significance of this component of the analysis. The deviations component represents the sum of squares of the deviations of the means of arrays from the regression line, due weight being given to the number of variates from which each mean was evaluated. Any one deviation from regression is the difference between the recorded array mean and the expected value X, as determined by regression. From the general regression equation,

$$X = M_x + b_{xy}(y - M_y)$$

Therefore, substituting the appropriate symbols from Table 53,

$$X_a = M_x + b_{xy}(m_y - M_y)$$

any advance on the existing methods is not likely to be of the perfectly obvious 100 per cent class but rather of the form of a 5 to 10 per cent increment. Thus, even if one particular treatment *A* is better than another treatment *B*, the difference is relatively slight, and in order to obtain satisfactory proof of this, field trials have to be carefully planned and accurately executed. It is essential to give the various treatments tested as nearly as possible similar conditions. As we shall see later, in field experiments there are certain influential factors over which man has little or no control, and this makes it even more necessary to ensure equality in those others over which full command can be exercised. Assuming that the original design of the experiment is technically sound, then accuracy of execution as regards such practical details as plot size, plant population, cultivation, harvesting, units of measurement, developmental studies, etc., is the *sine qua non* of successful experimentation. Such accuracy can be guaranteed only where skilled supervision and labor are available and, in consequence, the field experiment is a relatively expensive form of research. Moreover, the results from any one experiment are of limited application and hold good only for the particular soil and the particular season in which it was located. To establish the truth of any general law, a number of separate experiments in various soil types and over several seasons would have to be carried out and the aggregate data used to prove any particular hypothesis. Field experiments should therefore be the final stage in the solution of any given agricultural problem and should be resorted to only after the simpler and less expensive methods of eliminating any obviously unsatisfactory practices have been utilized. For example, in plant breeding, a variety trial should only be used as a test of a limited number of the best strains surviving after so many years' rigid selection from probably several hundred original types. Similarly, exacting field trials as a step toward improvement in a primitive agricultural community, where the general principles of good cultivation are continually flouted, would definitely be out of place. Under such conditions, the obvious line of advance is the establishment of a higher standard of field practice and a more intelligent appreciation of the elementary laws of crop growth. The value of any experiment must be gauged from the possible increase in national crop output, and in each problem, the simpler methods of achieving any given objective should be explored before expensive field trials are inaugurated.

The extremely variable nature of both soil and season forms an unavoidable obstacle to the easy solution of problems by field experimentation. Soils vary in fertility not only from acre to acre but even from foot to foot in any one field or plot. This makes it impossible to produce identical soil conditions for the various treatments, and numerous uniformity trials effectively illustrate the magnitude and ubiquity of the variation in yield arising solely from soil fertility differences. An apparent increment in favor of any one treatment may be entirely due to the fact that the plots of that particular treatment happen to be located on relatively fertile soil pockets, and the increment may have little or no relationship with the true potential yield values of the treatment. Similarly, with season, the prevailing climatic conditions in any one year may unduly favor one or two particular treatments at the expense of the remainder, when, actually, some slight change in climate might be sufficient to cause a radical change in the relative merits of the treatments tested. From experiments with 14 varieties of wheat over a period of 9 years, Engledow and Yule have demonstrated that, as a direct consequence of seasonal variation alone, varietal yields may fluctuate over a range of $\pm 7\frac{3}{4}$ of their mean value. Therefore, where the change in weather is at all marked, it is by no means impossible for the conclusions of one season's work to be practically reversed in the next. This brief discussion of the various problems with which the field experimentalist has to contend should be sufficient to prove that, as Engledow aptly quotes, "Alice soon came to the conclusion that it was a very difficult game indeed."

It is now necessary to examine the precautions that may be taken in order to offset, to some extent, the effects of the various environmental agencies at work and to arrive at an accurate appreciation of the relative merits of the various characters or treatments that it is desired to compare.

GENERAL PRINCIPLES

Experience.—The first essential of good experimentation is sound crop husbandry. This presupposes a detailed knowledge of the crop, the soil, and manurial requirements, the correct cultural technique, and accurate grading and evaluation of the produce. The chances of success are very much greater when a specialized experience of the crop has already been acquired. Where this experience is entirely lacking, *e.g.*, when a crop is first introduced into a new locality, large-scale experiments should not be attempted, as the field practice may be so artificial as to provide no fair test of the various factors under observation. The yield data represent only a part of the value of any experiment and should be augmented by regular field notes, recording the general progress of the crop and the more obvious differences between treatments at any particular stage of growth. Such notes can only be of critical value when the observer has the necessary basic experience of the crop.

Experimental Site.—The area of land selected for the experiment should conform to the general soil and environmental conditions under which it is intended to grow the crop commercially. To quote an extreme example, field experiments with sugar cane in England would be obviously of no economic value. Crop trials in unsuitable soils or in an abnormal environment may give results of a certain academic interest but are liable to be wrongly interpreted and misapplied by the practical farmer, especially if they are of a spectacular nature.

It is of the utmost importance to select the most uniform piece of ground available in order to minimize the effects of soil fertility differences between plots. A fair estimate of uniformity may be obtained from inspection of the previous crop, especially if such observations are supported by the experience of the resident farmer. Soil pits dug at frequent intervals are also helpful in determining whether the soil and subsoil are reasonably homogeneous or not. The importance of this question of initial soil uniformity cannot be too strongly emphasized. The theory that the improved technique used in field experiments today has made it immaterial whether the land is uniform or not is entirely false. Although with modern plot arrangements, the effects of soil heterogeneity can certainly be reduced in the analysis of the data, they cannot by any means be eradicated, and the more uniform the experimental site, the greater are the chances of obtaining a true evaluation of results.

Specification of Problem.—The nature of the problem should be exactly specified before any experimental plan is drawn up.

The choice of the particular treatments to be tested is especially important, as a relatively slight difference in the range covered, *e.g.*, in the quantities of fertilizer applied, may make all the difference between conclusive and inconclusive results. This presupposes an estimate of the magnitude of the difference between treatments that is likely to be obtained. The influence on the results of uncontrollable environmental factors makes the proof of small differences of the 2 to 3 per cent class of little practical significance. In a new line of research, it is advisable to select a range of treatments that theoretically will be bound to show relatively large treatment differences and then gradually to modify this range in succeeding experiments so as to bracket the optimum treatment. The advantages of complex experiments, where several different series of characters are included in a single large trial, have already been discussed (page **66**). Complex experiments require more expert supervision, careful recording, and a valid statistical interpretation of the data. The amount of complexity advisable will depend entirely on the experience of the staff in charge and on the facilities available in the way of labor, funds, and technical equipment. A simple experiment efficiently consummated is much to be preferred to a complex one in which the results are of doubtful accuracy because of possible errors of execution or interpretation.

The need for a high standard of accuracy in the field practice so as to give each plot as nearly as possible identical environmental conditions in the way of plot size, cultural attention, plant population, grading of produce, measurement of yields, etc., has already been mentioned. All these details should be specified when the experimental plan is first drawn up.

Replications.—For any particular treatment, a single large plot, even if it is several acres in extent, cannot give yield data of any value for comparative purposes. The experimental area should be divided into a number of similar plots, and so many plots allocated at random to each treatment. The greater the number of replications of any one series, the greater are the chances of obtaining an accurate result. There should be sufficient replications to ensure a fair measure of the mean and the standard deviation. It is not generally wise to reduce the number of replications of any one series below 4, and 6 to 10 replications are preferable. In the statistical interpretation of the results, the analysis of variance technique will usually be adopted, so that the standard deviation, on which the statistical comparison of mean differences is based, will be the square root of the error variance. It is advisable to plan the experiment so as to yield an error variance based on *not less* than 10—and preferably on 20 or more—degrees of freedom.

Type of Plot.—No particular size or shape of plot can be described as best in all circumstances. For a given number of replications, the larger the plot up to $\frac{1}{10}$ acre, the more accurate are the yield data likely to be. In plots above this size, the increase in soil heterogeneity within the plot will generally more than offset any advantage derived from increasing the plot area. Where the land or the other facilities are limited, a large number of small plots is generally to be preferred to a few large ones. A good average size for general utility purposes is $\frac{1}{40}$ acre.

The shape of the plot may be made anything from square or rectangular to a long narrow strip. The dimensions should be chosen so as to give a correct field layout and at the same time utilize most effectively the experimental site chosen. Where border effects are likely to occur, *i.e.*, where the crop in one treatment is likely to interfere with the proper growth of the crop at the edge of the adjacent plot of a second treatment, a non-experimental border of sufficient width must be left round each plot to ensure that these interference effects will not be reproduced in the yield data. This border is cultivated in exactly the same way as the plot to which it belongs, but the crop it carries is cut out before the experiment is harvested, leaving, for measurement, an effective plot unit equivalent to the area within the border. In this connection, it should be noted that the square plot is the area having the smallest perimeter.

Repetition.—The conclusions from any single experiment are only valid for the particular season and the particular soil in which the experiment was located. This makes it necessary to repeat the experiment over several years and in various soil types, so as to ascertain the exact range of environmental conditions for which the results can be stated to hold good. The standard test of significance is based on chances of 1 in 20, so that theoretically, over a large number of experiments there is a distinct possibility that a few of the conclusions will be inaccurate. This is an added reason why repeat experiments are necessary to supply adequate proof of the accuracy of any result of practical significance.   The scientist cannot afford to make serious errors in his recommendations.   Such mistakes in the past have sometimes led to a loss of confidence in his work by the very community which his researches are intended to benefit.

Arrangement of Plots.—The plots must be arranged in the field in a manner that will render possible a valid statistical interpretation of the yield data.   Statistical treatment is essential, if real differences between treatments are to be separated from purely fortuitous ones resulting from soil heterogeneity or other uncontrollable external agency.   Statistical significance is based on the assumption that the estimates of the means and standard deviations obtained from the data approximate to the true values that would have been obtained from an infinitely large number of plot replicates, *i.e.*, from the whole population.   This makes it essential that the location of the plots of any one treatment should be a random one.   On the other hand, it is known that there tends to be a close correlation between the soil fertility of adjacent plots, and in consequence, there is a much greater chance of demonstrating a real difference between two treatments *A* and *B* if they are located on contiguous plots than if they are widely separated.   There are various standard layouts which satisfy both these requirements.

Fisher's diagram in the Statistical Laboratory at Rothamsted effectively summarizes the principles from which modern experimental methods have been evolved.

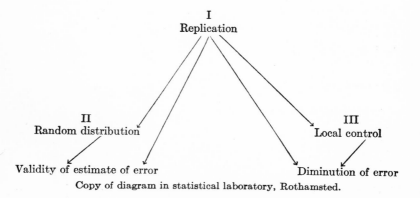

Copy of diagram in statistical laboratory, Rothamsted.

be the primary consideration. Each block should be divided into the same number of plots of a given size and shape. The number of plots in the block must be equal to the number of different treatments to be compared, so that if four varieties are under test, there will be four plots in each block. A single plot of each treatment must be included in each block. Thus every series is represented once in every block and, to this extent, the arrangement of the plots is a controlled one. The allocation of the treatments to the particular plots within a block should be a purely random one, determined by drawing lots or by other chance method. This randomization of treatments within each block is absolutely essential if the ordinary statistical tests of significance are to be validly applied. The total number of plots in the experiment is the number of treatments multiplied by the number of replications, *i.e.*, the number of plots in a block multiplied by the number of blocks.

Example 27.—It is possible to use the data from the wheat variety trial (Table 55) to exemplify the statistical technique applicable to a randomized block design. Actually, in this experiment, the arrangement of the 18 plots was not completely randomized, but the plots were grouped together in groups of three in juxtaposition, giving six similar blocks. Each treatment appeared once in each block, the arrangement of the three treatments within any one block being a random one. The serial numbers in the first column of Table 55 represent the six blocks and the yields of the three plots in each of these blocks are entered in the same line. Thus, the final column of Table 55 records the block totals. The data in this form are therefore representative of the yields from a randomized block layout made up of six blocks and three varieties.

The dispersion of these 18 variates, *i.e.*, the total sum of squares, is composite in character and is the result of

a. Differences between varieties.

b. Differences in soil fertility between blocks.

c. Unavoidable variation between similar variates, *i.e.*, error variance.

These component sums of squares can be assessed in the usual way, and the appropriate number of degrees of freedom allocated to each. The total and variety sums of squares have already been worked out in Example 26.

$$\text{Block S.S.} = \frac{33^2 + 42^2 + \cdots 33^2}{3} - \frac{216^2}{18} = 72$$

TABLE 57.—ANALYSIS OF VARIANCE OF RANDOMIZED BLOCK LAYOUT

Factor	S.S.	Degrees of freedom	Variance	F
Total....................	184	17		
Variety..................	93	2	46.50	←——24.48
Blocks..................	72	5	14.40	
Error...................	19	10	1.90	

Comparing this analysis with that given in Table 56, the most obvious difference is the very much smaller error variance here, showing that the variation in fertility between blocks is responsible for a relatively large share of the total dispersion.   In fact, if the F test is used to compare the block variance with that for error, the difference between them will be found to be definitely significant.   Even though the degrees of freedom of error have been reduced from 15 to 10, the elimination of the block component of the dispersion has greatly increased the chances of a positive F test.   The error variance in Table 57 really measures the unavoidable variation between plots in the same block— the aggregate within-block variation—after due allowance has been made for varietal differences.   It should now be clear why it is important to have the individual blocks as compact as possible.   The elimination of the block sum of squares from the estimate of error will not usually be advantageous unless there is a reasonable similarity in environmental conditions between the plots in any one block, and this is likely to occur only where the contiguity factor exists.   Very large blocks, usually a direct result of the inclusion of a large number of treatment comparisons in a single experiment, tend to annul the benefit that might be derived from using the block arrangement.

Standard error of any variety total of six replicates
$$= \sqrt{1.90 \times 6}$$
$$= 3.38$$
Reading of t ($n = 10$, $P = 0.05$) $= 2.228$
Significant difference between variety totals is one greater than
$$3.38 \times \sqrt{2} \times 2.228 = 10.63$$

On this basis, the treatments can be correctly graded on the following order: C, A, B. The block layout has reduced the estimate of error sufficiently to prove that the difference between the A and B varieties, which was nonsignificant on the original analysis, is actually a real difference in favor of A.

In most agricultural experiments, it is advisable to express the final statement of results in the units of measurement normally adopted commercially. This is most easily effected by calculating a single conversion factor by which the treatment totals and standard errors will have to be multiplied. If one assumes that a bushel of wheat weighs 62 pounds, the factor required to convert the wheat variety totals into bushels per acre will be

$$\frac{40}{6} \times \frac{2.25}{62} = 0.242$$

The results can now be recorded as

Variety A............ 16.7 ± 0.819 bu. per acre
Variety B............ 13.8 ± 0.819 bu. per acre
Variety C............ 21.8 ± 0.819 bu. per acre

and a clear statement of the final conclusions should follow. As a significant difference between means is approximately one greater than three times the standard error, it is possible for the reader to apply a simple test of the accuracy of the deductions.

Using the variable-squared method of computation, the following formulas summarize the calculations involved in the analysis of variance of data obtained from a randomized block experiment.

Let x = yield of any plot.

n = number of blocks, *i.e.*, number of replications of each treatment.

p = number of treatment comparisons, *i.e.*, number of plots in any one block.

T = grand total of all plot yields.

T_t = total yield of the n plots of any treatment.

T_b = total yield of the p plots in any block.

Then,

$$\text{Total S.S.} = \Sigma x^2 - \frac{T^2}{n \times p} \text{ with } np - 1 \text{ degrees of freedom}$$

$$\text{Treatment S.S.} = \frac{\Sigma T_t^2}{n} - \frac{T^2}{n \times p} \text{ with } p - 1 \text{ degrees of freedom}$$

$$\text{Block S.S.} = \frac{\Sigma T_b^2}{p} - \frac{T^2}{n \times p} \text{ with } n - 1 \text{ degrees of freedom}$$

Error S.S. = total S.S. − (treatment S.S. + block S.S.) with
$$(n - 1)(p - 1) \text{ degrees of freedom}$$

If the assumed-mean method of computation is adopted, the same formulas apply if x, T, T_b, T_t, represent the values recorded in the table of deviations instead of the actual plot yields and totals.

LATIN SQUARE

In this layout, the number of replications is made equal to the number of different treatments included in the experiment. If n is the number of replications (or treatments), then the total number of plots in the square will be n^2. The plots are arranged in a single large block so as to give the same number in line counting across or along the field, *i.e.*, the number of rows of plots is made the same as the number of columns. The dimensions of the individual plots may be anything from square to relatively long narrow strips, and the shape of the Latin square will be square or rectangular accordingly. The term "square" applied to this type of experiment is therefore used in the conventional sense of the word.

In the distribution of the treatments over the n^2 plots of the experiment, each treatment should appear once in each row and once in each column, but the allocation of the treatments within the rows and columns is otherwise at random. In order to ensure the validity of the F or z test used in the analysis of variance of the data, it is important to effect a correct randomization of the treatments within the rows and columns, so that the ultimate plot arrangement represents a random sample from all possible squares of the size selected. Especially with large squares, there may be some difficulty in evolving a square that will fulfill these various premises, and the easiest method of obtaining a satisfactory layout for any experiment is to make use of one of the standard forms given by Yates* for Latin squares from 3 × 3 up to 12 × 12. Then, by a random reshuffling of the rows, columns, and treatments, a valid layout will be obtained. The transformation of a 4 × 4 standard square for treatments designated A, B, C, D is given at the top of page 169.

* *Emp. J. Exp. Agr.*, 1: 236.

A B C D	*B C D A*	*B A C D*	*B C A D*
B C D A	*C D A B*	*C B D A*	*A B D C*
C D A B	*A B C D*	*A D B C*	*C D B A*
D A B C	*D A B C*	*D C A B*	*D A C B*
Standard	Reshuffling	Reshuffling	Reshuffling
square	of rows in	of columns	of the *A, B,*
	the order 2,	in the order	*C, D* treat-
	3, 1, 4, as se-	1, 4, 2, 3	ments on
	lected at		the basis of
	random		*C, B, A, D*

The advantage of the Latin-square layout lies in the fact that the plots can be grouped into *n* similar blocks in two distinct ways: (*a*) in accordance with the rows and (*b*) in accordance with the columns. Each of these components can be evaluated in the analysis of variance and, in consequence, it is possible to eliminate from the estimate of error the effects of soil fertility changes in two directions at right angles. As a control of the soil heterogeneity factor, the Latin square will generally be found to be an improvement on the randomized block layout. It has the disadvantage that it is much less flexible in character. For example, the number of replications is limited by the number of treatment comparisons, and where only three or four treatments are to be compared, the total number of plots in a single square will be only 9 or 16, respectively, which will not provide the minimum number of degrees of freedom advisable in order to ensure a fair estimate of the error variance.

The analysis of variance of a Latin-square experiment is fundamentally the same as that of the randomized block layout. The only modification is that the block sum of squares is virtually duplicated in the rows and in the columns, and the sum of squares attributed to each of these components separately is subtracted from the total sum of squares in estimating the error.

Example 28. Statistical Analysis of a 5 × 5 Latin Square for Data Taken from a Manurial Experiment with Sugar Cane.*— The five treatments were as follows:

A No manure

B Complete inorganic at rate of 90 lb. N, 375 lb. P_2O_5, and 60 lb. K_2O per acre

C 10 tons farmyard manure per acre

* *Trop. Agr.*, 9: 45.

D 20 tons farmyard manure per acre
E 30 tons farmyard manure per acre

TABLE 58.—YIELD OF PLANT CANE IN HALF-HUNDREDWEIGHTS PER $\frac{1}{30}$-ACRE PLOT AROUND AN ASSUMED MEAN OF 40 HALF-CWT.

Row	Column					Row totals	Treatment totals
	I	II	III	IV	V		
I	A 12 (−)	E 6 (+)	D 4 (−)	C 8 (−)	B 1 (+)	− 17	A −34
II	D 4	B 2	A 10	E 4	C 3	+ 3	B +23
III	B 9	A 7	C 0	D 1	E 7	+10	C −11
IV	C 3	D 2	E 7	B 5	A 5	+ 2	D − 4
V	E 7	C 3	B 6	A 0	D 3	+ 7	E +31
Column total.....	+5	−4	−1	+2	+3	Grand total + 5	

The treatment, row, and column totals are all tabulated, and the sum of squares belonging to each of these components can be calculated as usual.   For example,

$$\text{Row S.S.} = \frac{17^2 + 3^2 + 10^2 + 2^2 + 7^2}{5} - \frac{5^2}{25} = 89.2$$

There are five separate rows, so that the number of degrees of freedom of the row S.S. is 4; the same applies for columns and treatments.

TABLE 59.—ANALYSIS OF VARIANCE

Factor	S.S.	Degrees of freedom	Variance	F
Total..........................	800.0	24		
Rows..........................	89.2	4	22.3	
Columns.......................	10.0	4	2.5	
Treatments.....................	555.6	4	138.9⎰	11.48
Error..........................	145.2	12	12.1⎱	

The treatment variance is obviously significant. The standard error of any treatment total is $\sqrt{12.1 \times 5} = 7.778$. To convert this standard error or the corresponding treatment totals into tons per acre, it is necessary to multiply by the factor $\frac{30}{40 \times 5} = \frac{3}{20}$. The standard error expressed in tons per acre $= 7.778 \times \frac{3}{20} = 1.167$. The treatment totals given in Table 58 represent the total deviation of five plots round an assumed mean of 40 half-hundredweights, so that, before multiplying by the conversion factor for tons per acre, these totals must be expressed in absolute units of half-hundredweights per plot by adding to each 5×40 or 200 half-hundredweights. The mean yield of treatment A is therefore

$$(-34 + 200)\frac{3}{20} = \pm 7.778 \times \frac{3}{20} = 24.90 \pm 1.167;$$

the others are treated similarly.

Treatment		Tons per acre
A	No manure	24.90 ± 1.167
B	Complete inorganic	33.45 ± 1.167
C	10 tons farmyard manure	28.35 ± 1.167
D	20 tons farmyard manure	29.40 ± 1.167
E	30 tons farmyard manure	34.65 ± 1.167

Using three times the standard error,* *i.e.*, 3.5 tons per acre, as the measure of a significant difference, it is obvious that the most effective treatments are the complete inorganic mixture and the heaviest application of farmyard manure. The 10-ton dressing of farmyard manure just fails to show a significant increase over the control, which is, however, definitely worse than the remaining three treatments. The five treatments can therefore, be graded as follows:

Poor........ No Manure
Average..... 10 and 20 ton dressings of farmyard manure
Good....... Complete inorganic and 30 tons farmyard manure

* The exact critical difference is $\sqrt{12.1 \times 5 \times 2} \times 2.179 \times \frac{3}{20} = 3.59$ tons per acre.

The calculations involved in an analysis of variance of a Latin-square experiment are summarized in the following formulas:

Let x = yield of any plot.

n = number of replications of each treatment or number of rows or number of columns.

T = grand total of all n^2 plot yields.

T_t, T_r, T_c = total yield of n plots of any treatment, row, and column, respectively.

$$\text{Total S.S.} = \Sigma x^2 - \frac{T^2}{n^2} \text{ with } n^2 - 1 \text{ degrees of freedom}$$

$$\text{Treatment S.S.} = \frac{\Sigma T_t^2}{n} - \frac{T^2}{n^2} \text{ with } n - 1 \text{ degrees of freedom}$$

$$\text{Row S.S.} = \frac{\Sigma T_r^2}{n} - \frac{T^2}{n^2} \text{ with } n - 1 \text{ degrees of freedom}$$

$$\text{Column S.S.} = \frac{\Sigma T_c^2}{n} - \frac{T^2}{n^2} \text{ with } n - 1 \text{ degrees of freedom}$$

Error S.S. = total S.S. − (treatment S.S. + row S.S. + col. S.S.) with $(n - 1)(n - 2)$ degrees of freedom

Replication of Latin Squares.—In the Latin square, the number of replications is limited to the number of treatments tested, so that in small experiments the number of degrees of freedom on which the error variance is based becomes unduly depleted. This difficulty can be overcome if two or more Latin squares are used instead of a single one. A separate randomization of the treatments must be effected for each square. The statistical analysis becomes slightly more elaborate in order to take into account the fact that there may be considerable variation in the average soil fertility of the different squares. This is especially true if the squares are located some distance apart. In fact the treatments must be regarded as complex in nature consisting of actual treatment in combination with site, *i.e.*, of treatment and Latin square, and the interaction of these two factors should be evaluated.

Example 29. Statistical Analysis of a Cacao Manurial Experiment Consisting of Three 3 × 3 Latin Squares.—The fertilizers used were as follows:

A No manure
B $1\frac{1}{2}$ lb. superphosphate per tree
C 3 lb. superphosphate per tree

TABLE 60.—LAYOUT AND YIELD IN PODS PER TREE FROM $\frac{1}{15}$-ACRE PLOTS

	Square I				Square II				Square III			
				Row totals				Row totals				Row totals
	B 41	C 25	A 15	*81*	C 27	B 28	A 3	*58*	A 11	C 15	B 17	*43*
	A 20	B 32	C 24	*76*	A 4	C 17	B 9	*30*	B 24	A 14	C 33	*71*
	C 22	A 12	B 21	*55*	B 22	A 4	C 17	*43*	C 22	B 20	A 15	*57*
Column total...	*83*	*69*	*60*	*Total of I = 212*	*53*	*49*	*29*	*Total of II = 131*	*57*	*49*	*65*	*Total of III = 171*

Treatment	Treatment totals			Manurial treatment totals
	Square I	Square II	Square III	
A	47	11	40	98
B	94	59	61	214
C	71	61	70	202
Square total..............	212	131	171	*Grand total = 514*

The calculation of the total sum of squares from the 27 plot yields is perfectly straightforward, and amounts to **2,117.0**. From the table of the treatment totals

$$\text{Manurial treatment S.S.} = \frac{98^2 + 214^2 + 202^2}{9} - \frac{514^2}{27} = 904.4$$

$$\text{Square S.S.} = \frac{212^2 + 131^2 + 171^2}{9} - \frac{514^2}{27} = 364.6$$

Interaction: manures $\times$ squares

$$= \left(\frac{47^2 + 94^2 + \cdots 61^2 + 70^2}{3} - \frac{514^2}{27}\right) - (904.4 + 364.6)$$
$$= \mathbf{156.0}$$

In estimating this interaction sum of squares, the totals for each treatment in each square, as recorded in the second half of Table 60, are used, nine separate values in all. These values account for 8 degrees of freedom, of which 4 have already been used up in the square and manurial treatment sums of squares. This leaves 4 degrees of freedom for the interaction of squares.

As allowance has already been made for differences in fertility between the three squares, the row sum of squares must be calculated for each square separately, and the three separate values and degrees of freedom must be added together.

$$\text{Row S.S.} = \left(\frac{81^2+76^2+55^2}{3} - \frac{212^2}{9}\right) + \left(\frac{58^2+30^2+43^2}{3} - \frac{131^2}{9}\right)$$
$$+ \left(\frac{43^2 + 71^2 + 57^2}{3} - \frac{171^2}{9}\right) = 388.5$$

As there are three rows in each square, there will be $2 + 2 + 2$ degrees of freedom attached to this estimate. In a similar manner the column sum of squares can be calculated. It amounts to 242.4

TABLE 61.—ANALYSIS OF VARIANCE

Factor	S.S.	Degrees of free-dom	Variance	$\frac{1}{2} \log_e \text{variance}}{10}$	
Total...............	2117.0	26			
Manurial treatments...	904.4	2	452.2	1.9057	
Squares..............	364.6	2	182.3	1.4515	
Interaction: Squares × treatments.........	156.0	4	39.0		
Rows...............	388.5	6	64.7	0.9336	$z = 0.9237$
Columns.............	242.4	6	40.4		(signifi-
Error...............	61.1	6	10.2	0.0099	cant)

The column and interaction variances just fail to be significant on a probability of 0.05. The z test shows the rest of the factors in the analysis to be significantly greater than the error variance. The elimination of the soil heterogeneity effects in the evaluation of the variance of squares, rows, and columns has been beneficial in reducing the estimate of error.

A difference between totals for each manurial treatment greater than $\sqrt{10.2 \times 9 \times 2} \times 2.447 = 33.16$ is significant. This proves conclusively that there is a marked increase in yield as a result of the application of a phosphatic manure to the cacao trees, and that the double dressing of 3 pounds per tree shows no advantage over the single one.

GENERALIZATION OF RESULTS

The conclusion, as derived from the preceding statistical calculations, that $1\frac{1}{2}$ pounds of phosphate is the optimum rate for fertilizing cacao, only validly applies to the particular three soils or localities in which the squares were laid out. It is possible to use the same analysis of variance to achieve a more comprehensive conclusion which, on the average, can be said to be true for all cacao estates situated in the same general crop zone, and not only for sites showing similar soil and environmental factors to those actually occurring in the experiment. Let us suppose that three typical cacao estates at widely different centers had been selected at random for this experiment and that one square had been established on each estate. It follows that the soils of the three squares represent a random sample of the different soils in which cacao is likely to be planted in the locality. A fair estimate of the error variance likely to occur on this wide variety of soils will then be given by the treatment × square interaction, and results which are significant, as shown by the comparison between the treatment variance and that for this interaction of squares × treatments, are valid for the whole cacao crop of the locality.

The required variances taken from Table 61 are as follows:

Factor	S.S.	Degrees of freedom	Variance	$\frac{1}{2}\log_e$ of variance 10
Manurial treatment..............	904.4	2	452.2	1.9057
Interaction:				
Squares × treatments.......	156.0	4	39.0	0.6805
Difference...................				1.2252

The z test shows that the difference in the logarithmic column is significant. A difference between the treatment totals of nine plots greater than $\sqrt{39 \times 9 \times 2} \times 2.776 = 73.6$ is significant.

This again proves that the 1½-pound dressing is the best rate to use but, in addition, it has changed the practical significance of this result from one of rather limited application to one of general validity.

A similar type of statistical treatment will often be of value in the interpretation of the complete data from several years' experiments with the same material. In such serial experiments, it is exceedingly important to know whether the conclusions are likely to hold good for all ordinary seasonal vagaries, or whether, strictly speaking, they only really apply to the particular types of season prevailing in the experimental years. A comparison of the treatment variance with that for the treatment × season interaction is the most effective method at present available for settling the former query.

GROUPING OF TREATMENT COMPARISONS

In experiments in which one of the treatments is in the form of a control or standard type, it is often instructive to determine whether, on the average, the other treatments can be regarded as better or worse than the control. If the treatment variance is considered as a whole, it may even happen that the individual treatment differences are not sufficiently great to give a positive z test, whereas the isolation of one particular treatment comparison in the form of control *vs.* the average effect of the rest may indicate some definite response in the yields. The *modus operandi* is perfectly simple, being essentially the resolution of the total treatment variance among the various factors determining its value. Consider Example 28 in which the relative treatment yields for the total of five plots are as follows:

Treatment		Half-hundredweights
A	No manure	−34
B	Complete inorganic fertilizer	+23
C	10 tons farmyard manure	−11
D	20 tons farmyard manure	− 4
E	30 tons farmyard manure	+31
		+ 5

The total treatment sum of squares represents the aggregate effect of the difference between the fertilized and nonfertilized plots plus the variation due to the different types of fertilizer used. The totals for the nonmanured and manured treatments are for 5 and for 20 plots, respectively, so that the sum of squares for the first component

$$\text{Manure } vs. \text{ no manure} = \frac{34^2}{5} + \frac{39^2}{20} - \frac{5^2}{25}$$

$$= 306.25$$

$$\text{Then, S.S. type of manure} = \frac{23^2 + 11^2 + 4^2 + 31^2}{5} - \frac{39^2}{20}$$

$$= 249.35$$

$$\text{Total treatment S.S.} = 306.25 + 249.35$$

$$= 555.6 \text{ (as originally calculated, see Table 59)}$$

The fertilizers in turn can be divided into two distinct classes—organics and inorganics—and it is informative to carry the analysis a step further and resolve the sum of squares for manures into its components.

$$\text{S.S. organics } vs. \text{ inorganics} = \frac{23^2}{5} + \frac{16^2}{15} - \frac{39^2}{20}$$

$$= 46.82$$

S.S. quantity of

$$\text{farmyard manure} = \frac{11^2 + 4^2 + 31^2}{5} - \frac{16^2}{5}$$

$$= 202.53$$

$$\left.\begin{array}{c} 46.82 \\ \\ 202.53 \end{array}\right\} 249.35$$

TABLE 62.—ANALYSIS OF VARIANCE

Factor	S.S.	Degrees of freedom	Variance	$\frac{1}{2} \log_e \text{ of variance}$	z (by calculation)
Manure vs. no manure ...	306.25	1	306.25**	1.7109	1.6156
Organics vs. inorganics ...	46.82	1	46.82	0.7718	0.6765
Quantity of farmyard manure................	202.53	2	101.26**	1.1574	1.0621
Error (from Table 59)...	145.2	12	12.10	0.0953	

** Significant at the 1 per cent point. It should be noted that, in writing up experimental results, it is not generally considered necessary to tabulate the calculated values of F or z. The customary practice is to mark variances which are significant at the 5 per cent point with one star, and those significant at the 1 per cent point with two stars.

After allocating to each its correct share of the total treatment degrees of freedom, the F or z test can be used to test the significance of any of these components of the treatment variance.

The first and third components are significant, but there is no significance in the comparison of organics vs. inorganics. Manuring of cane, as judged by the average result of the four dressings tested, leads to a definite increase in yield; a heavy application of farmyard manure produces a much bigger response than a light one; a complete inorganic fertilizer produced a yield increment equivalent to that of a heavy dressing of farmyard manure.

ORTHOGONALITY

The analysis of variance technique as applied to research data is valid only when the experimental design is orthogonal. Yates defines *orthogonality* as "that property of the design which ensures that the different classes of effects to which the experimental material is subject shall be capable of direct and separate estimation without any entanglement." A fundamental principle of the orthogonal layout is that any real differences between the treatments in one series should not affect the relative values for any of the other series in the experiment. To ensure this, it is advisable to use the same number of replicates for each treatment in any one series. This should effect a balanced and orthogonal experimental design. Apart from any question of orthogonality, equal numbers of replicates are desirable in order to keep the statistical calculations as simple as possible. In a simple randomized block experiment with five blocks and two treatments, each treatment occurs once in each block; any fertility difference between the blocks as a whole will be reflected proportionately in all the treatments, so that treatment differences are not affected by variation between the blocks. Similarly, each block contains one plot of every treatment so that any difference between the blocks is not affected by treatment differences. Treatment and block variances are entirely independent and can be calculated separately. The layout is orthogonal, and the analysis of variance technique can be validly applied to the data.

If, by accident, two plots of one treatment and none of the second were included in one of the blocks, the whole balance between treatments and blocks is upset, as shown in the following diagram:

Treat-ment	Blocks					No. of variates in each treatment
	I	II	III	IV	V	
A	*x*	*x*	*xx*	*x*	*x*	6
B	*x*	*x*		*x*	*x*	4

Suppose, for example, that the soil fertility in block III is distinctly above average, the mean yield of treatment *A* will be above and that of treatment *B* will be below their true potential values. The resultant conclusion regarding the relative merits of the two treatments might be erroneous. The error variance from a randomized block design is really a measure of the interaction between blocks and treatments. Normally, in a layout of the above type, the interaction might be assessed directly from the difference in the $A - B$ values for each block. Here, however, treatment differences are entangled or confounded with the block differences, and the interaction or error variance might also be affected by the mistake in block III. The results would probably be markedly falsified. The layout is therefore no longer orthogonal, and the ordinary analysis of variance technique cannot be validly applied. A modified and very much more complicated method of statistical analysis, entailing the fitting of constants, would be required. Alternatively, the between- and within-treatment variance could be calculated and used to compare the treatments, taking into account the different number of variates in the two series. Although this method is permissible, it makes no allowance for the variation in fertility between blocks and would almost certainly give an unnecessarily high estimate of error and detract from the precision of the experiment.

The same criticism of nonorthogonality would be true if the above mistake occurred in a factorial experiment in which the numbers I to V represented a second treatment series superimposed on the *A* and *B* treatments and if several replications of each treatment type were included. The data could still apparently be analyzed by the ordinary analysis of variance procedure, but the nonorthogonal layout might lead to a false estimate not only of the treatment variances but also of the error variance. The example cited represents a relatively slight deviation from orthogonality, and the results by the ordinary method of analysis might not be greatly different from the correct values for the experiment. This could not be considered as any excuse for knowingly applying a faulty statistical technique. The more extreme the degree of nonorthogonality, the greater will the falsification of the results by a simple analysis of variance tend to be. Lack of recognition in the past of the principle of orthogonality has led to the incorrect use of the analysis of variance technique and subsequent erroneous interpretation of experimental data. In planning new experiments, the novice would be well advised to adopt only standardized designs in which a correct balance between the different components of the analysis of variance is ensured.

INCOMPLETE RECORDS

In field experiments, it is sometimes impossible, for one reason or another, to obtain the correct yield data for certain plots. This may be the result of loss of the actual yield figures, mistakes at harvest, serious damage to isolated plots by vermin or flooding, or other external agencies. The experimental precision is bound to be somewhat impaired, as, of course, the original orthogonal design is upset even when only a single variate is missing. If an accurate appreciation of the relative treatment effects is to be obtained, the statistical technique has to be modified.

Consider first of all the simplest case of a randomized block layout in which only a single plot yield is missing. A valid but rather inefficient method of tackling this case would be to ignore all treatment yields in the block in which the missing plot was located and to carry out a straightforward analysis of variance of the data from the remaining $n - 1$ blocks. This method is simple but has the obvious disadvantage of reducing the number of replications of each treatment by unity, of lowering the number of degrees of freedom of error, and of markedly decreasing the precision of the experiment.

A second but inaccurate method which has been used in the past is to make allowance in computing the component sums of squares for the fact that one of the treatments and one of the blocks has one replicate less than the remainder. This makes the arithmetical calculations slightly more complicated than would have been the case had the observations been complete. It has the much bigger disadvantage that, owing to the non-orthogonal nature of the data, it is statistically unsound and may lead to false conclusions.

The best method of tackling the problem is to apply Yates' missing plot technique* in which the remainder of the data is used to provide a logical estimate of the missing yield. In this way, the required degree of orthogonality is recovered, and a simple analysis of variance of the completed data can then be effected, provided an appropriate modification in the number of degrees of freedom allocated to error and in the estimation of the standard errors of the various treatments is incorporated. It is proposed to use the data from Table 55 with one variate omitted to illustrate the practical application of these last two alternatives and demonstrate that even this slight deviation from normality must be given due weight in the statistical interpretation of the results.

Example 30. Analysis of Data from Randomized Block Experiment in Which One of the Plot Yields from Block V Is Lost.—The data are otherwise the same as recorded in Table 55.

TABLE 63.—YIELD OF WHEAT IN KILOGRAMS PER PLOT

Blocks	Varieties			Block total
	A	B	C	
I	8	9	16	33
II	14	11	17	42
III	12	10	14	36
IV	8	7	12	27
V	16	11	x	27
VI	11	9	13	33
Variety total............	69	57	72	Grand total 198
Variety mean............	11.5	9.5	14.4	

In a randomized block experiment an estimate of the potential yield of the missing plot can be obtained from the formula

* *Emp. J. Exp. Agr.*, 1: 129–142.

$$x = \frac{n \times T_v + p \times T_s - T}{(n-1)(p-1)}$$

when x = missing-plot yield.

n = number of blocks or replicates.

p = number of treatments.

v = block in which missing plot is located.

T_v = total of remaining $p - 1$ plots in block v.

s = treatment in which missing plot occurs.

T_s = total of remaining $n - 1$ plots in treatment s.

T = grand total of all available $np - 1$ plots.

Applying this equation to provide an estimate of the missing yield in Table 63 for variety C in block V,

$$x = \frac{6 \times 27 + 3 \times 72 - 198}{10} = 18$$

This value happens to have worked out at exactly the yield figure recorded for this plot in the original data of Table 55. The component sums of squares including the estimate of the missing plot will be the same as those worked out in Table 57 for the original analysis of variance. When a single plot yield is missing, 1 degree of freedom is used up in the estimation of the missing variate, which reduces the total available degrees of freedom to $np - 2$. This in turn cuts down by unity the number of degrees of freedom normally attributed to error in an experiment of this particular layout. The appropriate analysis of variance of the data on this basis is appended.

TABLE 64.—ANALYSIS OF VARIANCE DERIVED FROM "MISSING-PLOT" TECHNIQUE

Factor	S.S. (from Table 57)	Degrees of freedom	Variance
Total......................	184	16	
Blocks.....................	72	5	
Varieties..................	93	2	46.50**
Error......................	19	9	2.11

** Significant at the 1 per cent point. It should be noted that, in writing up experimental results, it is not generally considered necessary to tabulate the calculated values of F or z. The customary practice is to mark variances which are significant at the 5 per cent point with one star, and those significant at the 1 per cent point with two stars.

The variety variance is significantly greater than the error variance. Actually the use of the missing-plot technique tends to give a treatment variance slightly in excess of its true value, but the exaggeration is negligible.

For the comparison of treatments, other than treatment s with the missing plot, the usual formulas for calculating the standard errors apply, *viz.*,

$$E = \sqrt{\frac{\text{error variance}}{n}} = \sqrt{\frac{\sigma^2}{n}}$$

Thus, in comparing the means of treatments A and B,

$$E_D = \sqrt{\frac{2.11 \times 2}{6}} = 0.84$$

A significant difference between the means of treatments A and B is one greater than 0.84×2.262 or 1.90. Variety A is therefore better than variety B.

In order to compare treatment s with any other treatment, a revised value of E_D has to be calculated. An approximate but satisfactory estimation of this value will be obtained provided:

a. The number of replications of treatment s is assumed to be $n - 1$, even though the estimate of the missing-plot yield has been used in determining the mean of the treatment.

b. Only one-half instead of one replication is accorded to the extra plot of the second treatment in block v.

Then

$$E_D = \sqrt{\frac{\sigma^2}{n - 1} + \frac{\sigma^2}{n - \frac{1}{2}}}$$

for comparing the mean of treatment s and any other treatment mean. Thus, in the example cited, for the comparison of treatment C with either A or B,

$$E_D = \sqrt{\frac{2.11}{5} + \frac{2.11}{5.5}} = 0.90$$

A significant difference between means is one greater than $0.90 \times 2.262 = 2.035$. On this basis, variety C is better than either A or B.

In order to illustrate the necessity of applying the missing-plot technique, it is proposed to use the same data to carry out a direct analysis of variance, ignoring the fact that the layout has become nonorthogonal.

$$\text{Total S.S.} = 8^2 + 14^2 + \cdots 12^2 + 13^2 - \frac{198^2}{17} =$$
$$145.9 \text{ with 16 degrees of freedom}$$

$$\text{Block S.S.} = \frac{33^2 + 42^2 + 36^2 + 27^2 + 33^2}{3} + \frac{27^2}{2} - \frac{198^2}{17} =$$
$$44.1 \text{ with 5 degrees of freedom}$$

$$\text{Variety S.S.} = \frac{69^2 + 57^2}{6} + \frac{72^2}{5} - \frac{198^2}{17} =$$
$$65.7 \text{ with 2 degrees of freedom}$$

$$\text{Error S.S.} = 145.9 - (44.1 + 65.7) =$$
$$36.1 \text{ with 9 degrees of freedom}$$

The error variance is $\frac{36.1}{9} = 4.01$. On this basis the standard error of the difference between the means of varieties A and B is $\sqrt{\frac{4.01}{6}} \times 2 = 1.16$. This test would seem to show that the difference is nonsignificant, whereas by using the more accurate missing-plot technique, this difference has already been proved significant. The entanglement of the block and treatment differences, as a result of the missing plot in block v, invalidates a simple analysis of variance of the available data.

Estimation of a Missing Plot in a Latin Square.—In a Latin square with one missing plot the same general principles, regarding the best analysis of variance to use, hold good. In this case, the formula for estimating the missing-plot yield x is

$$x = \frac{n(T_s + T_C + T_R) - 2T}{(n - 1)(n - 2)}$$

where T_C = the total of the remaining $n - 1$ plots in the column with the missing plot.

T_R = the total of the remaining $n - 1$ plots in the row with the missing plot.

The notation is otherwise as detailed for the randomized block layout.

Then the standard error of the difference between the mean of treatment *s* and any other treatment mean

$$E_D = \sqrt{\frac{\sigma^2}{n-1} + \frac{\sigma^2}{n - \frac{2}{3}}}$$

Analysis of Variance When Several Plots Are Missing.—An extension of this method of estimating the yield of a missing plot can be used for data in which several plot yields are missing. This is effected by putting in an arbitrary approximation for all the missing-plot yields except one and applying the formulas already given for estimating the value of this one. This value is then entered and used in the determination of the value of the second missing plot; and so on in sequence for each plot in turn, the total for the table being altered in accordance with each new value obtained.

The whole process should be repeated a second time with the first estimates entered, reestimating again for each plot in turn. This will give yields that are accurate within 0.01 of the required values.

The same general rules regarding the analysis of variance and the calculation of the standard errors, as already discussed for a single blank entry in the data, hold good when there are several missing plots. When there are more than three missing plots, the treatment variance may be significantly exaggerated. In more extreme cases, it is questionable whether elaborate statistical computation can effectively take the place of actual field data.

Example 31.—As an example of the procedure, the analysis for the following 5 × 5 Latin square, with three missing-plot yields (*x*, *y*, and *z*), is given in detail.

Entering the mean value (Table 65) as an arbitrary estimate of the yield of plot *y* and of plot *z*, substitution in the formula for a missing plot in a Latin square gives

$$x_1 = \frac{5(77 + 74 + 86) - 2 \times 480}{4 \times 3} = 18.7$$

Sufficient accuracy will be obtained if the calculations are taken to one place of decimals beyond that used for the plot yields.

Using this value for x and the same arbitrary value of 20 for z,

$$y_1 = \frac{5(62 + 86 + 84.7) - 2 \times 478.7^*}{12} = 17.2$$

Then, substituting this value for y,

$$z_1 = \frac{5(75.7 + 83.2 + 79) - 2 \times 475.9^*}{12} = 19.8$$

Repeating this process for each plot in turn so as to correct the preliminary estimates x_1, y_1, z_1,

$$x = \frac{5(76.8 + 74 + 83.2) - 2 \times 475.7^*}{12} = 18.2$$

Similarly y on recalculation becomes 17.4, and z on recalculation becomes 19.8.

Obviously there will be little advantage in quoting the missing-plot yields in smaller units than the actual ones, and in the

TABLE 65.—LAYOUT OF 5 × 5 SQUARE AND YIELD OF SUGAR CANE IN HUNDREDWEIGHTS PER $\frac{1}{40}$-ACRE PLOT FOR 5 VARIETIES A, B, C, D, AND E.

A	E	D	C	B
14	22	20	18	25
D	B	A	E	C
19	21	16	23	18
B	A	C	D	E
23	15	20	18	23
C	D	E	B	A
21	x	24	21	y
E	C	B	A	D
23	16	23	17	z

Total of the 22 available plot yields = 440 cwt.
Mean of the 22 available plot yields = 20 cwt. per plot

* The revised total for 24 plots when the latest estimate is entered in the table.

following analysis of variance, the nearest integer for these estimates has been used, *viz.:*

$$x = 18$$
$$y = 17$$
$$z = 20$$

TABLE 66.—ANALYSIS OF VARIANCE OF COMPLETED DATA

Factor	S.S.	Degree of freedom	Variance
Total..	220	21†	
Rows..	2	4	
Columns....................................	17	4	
Varieties...................................	181	4	45.2**
Error.......................................	20	9	2.2

** Significant at the 1 per cent point.
† A deduction of 3 degrees of freedom for the three missing plots.

The treatment variance is clearly significant. The variety means for the completed table are as follows:

Hundredweights per plot
A............15.8
B............22.6
C............18.6
D............19.0
E............23.0

Varieties *B* and *E* have apparently given high yields and *A* a low yield.

It would be interesting to test further whether *D* is significantly better than *A* and *E* than *D*. The appropriate standard errors for these comparisons are required. Here again, the number of replications accorded to each mean is based primarily on the total number of actual yields obtained for that treatment in the field records. Furthermore, any treatment mean is accorded only two-thirds of a replication for each field plot located in a row or a column where the opposite treatment shows a missing plot; and only one-third of a replication if the second treatment is missing in both row and column. On this basis, in a comparison of varieties *A* and *D*, the number of replications of *A* is equivalent to 3⅓ and of *D* to 3, so that

Standard error of difference between means of A and $D =$

$$\sqrt{\frac{2.2}{10\frac{2}{3}} + \frac{2.2}{3}} = 1.18$$

Significant difference is one $> 1.18 \times 2.262 = 2.69$

The difference between means is 3.2 cwt. and therefore significant. Similarly, for the comparison of varieties D and E,

standard error of difference between means $= \sqrt{\frac{2.2}{3} + \frac{2.2}{11\frac{1}{3}}} = 1.15$

The difference between the means is 4, and therefore also significant. The varieties can now be accurately graded.

B and E High yielders
C and D Average yielders
A Low yielder

CHAPTER VIII

SERIAL AND PERENNIAL CROP EXPERIMENTS

SERIAL EXPERIMENTS

Before it is advisable to recommend the modification of existing field practice, any important experiment should be repeated for at least 3 years in order to be sure that the results hold good under varying seasonal conditions. The final recommendations should be based on the accumulated data of all the experiments. There are various ways of effecting a comprehensive interpretation of such serial experiments. As the yield data for each year will normally be analyzed as soon as the records reach the laboratory, a simple method is to make a résumé of the individual results and use this accumulated evidence to assess the real differences between treatments. For example, if one variety was the best in three successive years, this could be regarded as conclusive proof of its superiority. If, on the other hand, this variety was the best in the first 2 years but below average in the third, any statement of its performance would require some seasonal qualification.

This method of assessing the results is perfectly valid, but it does not make the fullest use of the available data. It is possible to construct a single analysis of variance for the combined records for the three seasons, and ascertain from this the exact significance of the various component factors. In such an analysis the seasonal component will generally account for a good share of the total dispersion of the variates.

Example 32. Statistical Analysis of Combined Data from Two Sugar Cane Variety Trials for Years 1933 and 1934, Respectively.

The variance for season includes that due to the difference in soil fertility between the two experiments as a whole, so that the sum of squares and degrees of freedom for blocks are the aggregate values for the two experiments taken separately. It will also

TABLE 67.—YIELD OF CANE IN QUARTERS PER $\frac{1}{40}$-ACRE PLOT

Variety	Exp. I (1933)						Exp. II (1934)						Variety total for Exp. I and II
	Blocks					Variety total for Exp. I	Blocks					Variety total for Exp. II	
	1	2	3	4	5		1	2	3	4	5		
St. Croix $1\frac{3}{4}$	41	44	45	45	44	219	38	35	41	39	45	198	417
B.H. $1\frac{9}{12}$...	52	61	58	66	49	286	50	51	48	64	63	276	562
Uba.........	44	54	51	52	60	261	46	37	47	49	48	227	488
B. 726......	56	50	60	56	60	282	47	57	55	65	46	270	552
Co. 213......	51	56	61	64	63	295	43	51	56	56	72	278	573
Block total..	244	265	275	283	276	1343	224	231	247	273	274	1249	2592

be necessary to estimate the interaction between variety and
season to ascertain whether or not the varieties have shown
any differential response to the change in climatic conditions
between 1933 and 1934.

TABLE 68.—ANALYSIS OF VARIANCE

Factor	S.S.	Degrees of freedom	Variance
Total.................................	3526.7	49	
Varieties.............................	1721.7	4	430.4**
Seasons..............................	176.7	1	176.7*
Interaction: Season × variety............	36.3	4	9.1
Blocks...............................	614.4	8	76.8
Error................................	977.6	32	30.5

* Significant at 5 per cent point.
** Significant at 1 per cent point.

The only significant components in this analysis are variety
and season. The interaction is nonsignificant, and it can be
assumed that the varieties have maintained the same relative
position for the 2 years. The conversion factor required to
express the variety totals in tons per acre is one-twentieth.
The mean yields then become:

and the scion. Where the experiment is to be superimposed on established plantations, a locality in which the trees are all of one age class should be selected.

Size of Plot.—On account of the wide spacing required by most orchard crops, plots of larger size than those recommended for annual crops will usually be necessary. Each plot should contain 10 or more trees; with an average orchard spacing, this will give a plot size of approximately ⅙ acre.

Layout.—Probably the Latin square is to be preferred, as any one experiment will extend over a considerable area of land, and this arrangement most effectively reduces the error due to soil fertility differences.

Cultural Treatment.—The trees should be given parallel treatment as regards pruning, harvesting, soil cultivation, etc. Even the difference in skill and care between two expert pruners or pickers may be sufficiently large to produce a significant effect on the ultimate yields.

Border Rows.—Nonexperimental guard rows between plots will generally be required to obviate edge interference and prevent any one treatment from affecting the growth of the trees on adjacent plots. The most efficient system, but one which utilizes a large area, is to establish a separate guard row around every plot, so that between the effective plot units there will always be two guard rows. In this system, each tree in any one border row is given the same treatment as the plot to which it belongs, but the yields of the border trees are not entered in the experimental records. With wide-spaced orchard crops, the area of land occupied by the guard rows will often be greater than that of the actual experimental plots. In this connection it should be noted that the greater the number of trees in the experimental plot the smaller will be the proportion of land under border rows. To quote an extreme example, to isolate effectively a plot made up of a single tree will require 8 border trees on a rectangular layout, or four border trees on a triangular or quincuncial layout. Whereas, on a square plot of 16 trees, only 20 guard trees will be necessary, reducing the proportion of border to experimental plants from 4:1 to 5:4. Similarly the shape of the plot is important. A plot consisting of a double row with 8 trees in each will require 24 guard trees as compared with 20 for the same number of trees on a square layout. A single row of 16 trees would need no less than 38 border units.   These features are illustrated in diagrammatic form below.

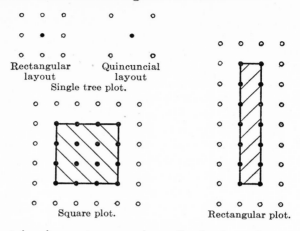

Rectangular layout   Quincuncial layout
Single tree plot.

Square plot.   Rectangular plot.

In certain circumstances, where the land or the number of trees of a given age class is limited, it may be necessary to compromise in order to obtain the requisite number of replications.   One method of doing this is to allow for only a single or common guard row between plots, choosing a type of treatment intermediate in character between those being tested.   For example, in a variety test an entirely different species might be selected for the guard rows; this has the added advantage of effectively outlining the experimental plots.   When the use of a single guard row is considered practicable, the nonexperimental area will be reduced by almost 50 per cent.   Another com-

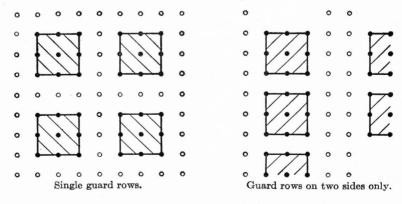

Single guard rows.   Guard rows on two sides only.

promise is to plant guard rows along only the two sides of each plot, so that every tree is surrounded on at least three sides by similar units.

Records.—Most authorities recommend the separate recording of the yields of every single tree in the experiment. Many purely commercial growers keep such records in order to allow them to eradicate nonprofitable yielders. In experimental work, individual tree records make it possible to ascertain the variation within plots and may even demonstrate the advisability of eliminating particular blocks showing undesirable heterogeneity. Yield data for each tree often prove invaluable in planning further experiments. It is sometimes possible to use such previous records to work out the analysis of covariance in order to effect a valid reduction in the estimate of the error variance by means of the regression function (Chap. IX).

Most trees have a definite fruiting period during the year, and, in consequence, the yield data can be grouped according to year as well as according to treatment and block. In orchard crops where there is a tendency to yield heavily every second year, statistical analysis applied to the combined yield of plots for two consecutive harvests has obvious advantages.

The yield data alone represent only a small part of the total information that should be collected. In many experiments other factors are equally important in estimating the effects of treatment, *e.g.*, girth increment, spread of the tree, annual wood growth, fruit-bud productivity, and the percentage of shedding, etc. Observations regarding the general tone and vigor of the trees, the prevalence of fungal and insect attack, and other similar cultural details are also of value. All these points serve to emphasize the fact that experimentation with a perennial crop must be tackled in earnest from the outset. It is a lengthy, expensive, and often disappointing task. Before conclusive results can be expected, the experiment must be carefully designed and efficiently supervised from start to finish. Whatever system is followed, the cost of experimentation will be considerable, and it is essential to justify this outlay by scrupulous attention to detail, which is the only way of approaching the ultimate objective.

Classification of Produce.—The bulk yield per plot is of only limited utility. The produce after harvest usually has to be classified into first, second, third, and scrap grades; the statistical analysis may be limited to the total yields or to yields per plot of marketable produce, but an estimate of the percentage of each quality in the salable fruit is also essential if correct conclusions are to be formed.   With many crops chemical analysis may be deemed necessary in order to assess the relative quality of the produce.

STATISTICAL ANALYSIS OF DATA FROM PERENNIAL CROPS

Most experiments with perennial crops will have to continue for a period of several years in order to permit of an accurate comparison of the various treatments.   An analysis of each season's data separately is perfectly valid, and the accumulated evidence thus obtained may be satisfactorily conclusive.   As a general rule, however, the complete data for the whole of the experimental period should be coordinated in a single table, and to this extent the records resemble those for serial experiments.   With perennial crops there is an important difference in that the randomization is not changed, and the yield data for each successive year are for the same plots and the same plants.   The statistical analysis has to be modified accordingly, because a series of successive harvests or pickings from any plot does not entail any increase in the number of replications on which the measure of plot variation will be based.   This principle must not be forgotten in the application of statistics to the results.   On the other hand, the total yield from any plot is divisible into so many separate subunits according to season, and it may be important to assess the relative response of treatment to season.   The analysis of variance should therefore be of the error (a) and error (b) type, in which the former is used to assess the aggregate difference between treatments for the whole period covered by the experiment and the latter to measure any differential response of the treatments to the varying seasonal conditions.

Example 33.   Statistical Analysis of Two Years' Yield Data from a Perennial Crop.—To illustrate the difference in the statistical technique, it will be assumed that the data from Table 67 for a serial experiment represent instead the plant cane and first ratoon crop from successive harvests from the same plots in 1933 and 1934.   The analysis of variance appended is one appropriate to such a premise.

TABLE 69.—YIELD OF PLANT CANE AND FIRST RATOON CROPS IN QUARTERS PER $\frac{1}{40}$-ACRE PLOT

Variety	Harvest	Blocks					Total across
		1	2	3	4	5	
St. Croix $1\frac{3}{4}$..	1933	41	44	45	45	44	219
	1934	38	35	41	39	45	198
	Total	*79*	*79*	*86*	*84*	*89*	*417*
B.H. $1\frac{9}{12}$.....	1933	52	61	58	66	49	286
	1934	50	51	48	64	63	276
	Total	*102*	*112*	*106*	*130*	*112*	*562*
Uba.........	1933	44	54	51	52	60	261
	1934	46	37	47	49	48	227
	Total	*90*	*91*	*98*	*101*	*108*	*488*
B. 726........	1933	56	50	60	56	60	282
	1934	47	57	55	65	46	270
	Total	*103*	*107*	*115*	*121*	*106*	*552*
Co. 213.......	1933	51	56	61	64	63	295
	1934	43	51	56	56	72	278
	Total	*94*	*107*	*117*	*120*	*135*	*573*
Block total......		*468*	*496*	*522*	*556*	*550*	*2,592 grand total*
Block × season total........	1933	244	265	275	283	276	1,343
	1934	224	231	247	273	274	1,249

A simple randomized block analysis of the values shown in italics, *i.e.*, of the aggregate yield of each of the 25 plots for both harvests, would determine the best varieties on the average result of the two seasons' crop. The yield of the ratoon crop, relative to that of the plant cane, is of considerable significance, as the number of years the crop should be left in the field before replanting becomes necessary depends on this factor. This makes it advisable to carry out a more detailed analysis of the complete data in order to obtain an accurate statistical evaluation of the relative behavior of the varieties for each harvest. It will be assumed that the student is capable of using Table 69 to calculate any particular component of the analysis appended, the units in which the results are expressed being the plot yields of one season. This means that the sums of squares and variances of all the factors in the analysis, including error (*a*), are expressed in subunits.

TABLE 70.—ANALYSIS OF VARIANCE

Factor	S.S.	Degrees of freedom	Variance
Total for individual harvests............	3,526.7	49	
1933–1934 aggregate yields.............	2,676.7	24	
Blocks...............................	*536.7*	*4*	*134.2***
Varieties............................	*1,721.7*	*4*	*430.4***
Error (a)...........................	*408.3*	*16*	*25.5*
Season..............................	176.7	1	176.7*
Interactions:			
Season × variety..................	36.3	4	9.1
Season × blocks..................	67.7	4	16.9
Error (*b*)..........................	569.3	16	35.6

*Significant at 5 per cent point.
**Significant at 1 per cent point.

If this analysis is compared with that given in Table 68, it will be seen that the difference is only one of allocation of the total dispersion between its various components. The aggregate sum of squares for error (*a*) and error (*b*) is identical with that given originally under the error factor. The sum of squares for blocks added to that for the interaction of season × blocks is the same as the block sum of squares in Table 68. The other factors are unchanged.

In assessing results on this new allocation, error (*a*) should be used for the comparison of values derived from the aggregate plot yields for the two seasons, which in this example will be the block and the variety totals. In calculating the standard error of these totals, it is important to remember that the analysis is in subunit values and that each total represents the aggregate of so many subunits. Error (*b*) is the correct estimate of variance for the other factors in which the comparable means depend on the way the total plot yields are apportioned between the two harvests. The hypothesis that the data are from two successive harvests of a perennial crop introduces only a minor change in the final conclusions. On the new basis, the block sum of squares

and not merely a temporary response to the additional nutrient. The potash has been entirely ineffectual.

ANALYSIS OF GROUPED DATA WHEN DIFFERENT ASSUMED MEANS ARE USED FOR EACH GROUP

The advantage of using an appropriate assumed mean in order to reduce the amount of arithmetical calculation in the computation of an analysis of variance has already been noted. With accumulated data from perennial crops or from serial experiments over several years, the variation in the average yield from season to season is often so great that it will annul much of the advantage of using the ordinary assumed-mean technique. For example, for the yield data of Table 71, an assumed-mean value of 360 pounds might be selected as a suitable approximation to the true mean, but the variation in yield from 1933 to 1935 is such that the deviation of many of the recorded yields from this assumed mean will run to three digits and the squares of these deviations to five digits. It is obvious that such large deviations would be avoided if a different, but appropriate, assumed mean was used for the data of each year. This may actually be done and, provided a suitable modification in the statistical procedure is introduced, the detailed analysis of variance, as tabulated in Table 72, may be derived with con-

TABLE 73.—TREATMENT YIELDS OF TEA IN POUNDS OF DRY MATTER PER FIVE PLOTS, AROUND ASSUMED-MEAN VALUES APPROPRIATE TO EACH SEASON

Season	Assumed mean	Treatments						Season total	Season × nitrogen total			Season × potash total	
		N_0K_0	N_0K_1	N_1K_0	N_1K_1	N_2K_0	N_2K_1		N_0	N_1	N_2	K_0	K_1
1933	260	−6	+9	−2	+3	−1	+3	+18	−15	+5	+2	−9	+9
1934	470	4	31	1	15	6	42	+29	35	16	48	3	26
1935	320	34	29	6	35	76	61	+115	63	41	137	48	67
Total		−44	−69	+5	+47	+81	+106	Grand total +126	−113	+52	+187	+42	+84

−113   +52   +187

siderable reduction in the amount of routine arithmetic. As an illustration of the statistical technique, the data from Table 71 have been rearranged in Table 73 with the yields recorded around assumed means of

260 lb. for the year 1933,
470 lb. for the year 1934,
320 lb. for the year 1935,

When the evaluation of any factor in the analysis of variance is derived from treatment totals representing aggregate values for all three seasons, the arithmetical procedure is exactly the same as that adopted when only one assumed mean has been used. Remembering that the yields recorded represent the totals for five plots or replicates and that there are therefore 90 variates in all, the

$$\text{General C.F.} = \frac{\text{Grand total}^2}{90} = \frac{126^2}{90} = 176.4$$

$$\text{S.S. nitrogen} = \frac{113^2 + 52^2 + 187^2}{30} - \text{C.F.} = 1505.0$$

$$\text{S.S. potash} = \frac{42^2 + 84^2}{45} - \text{C.F.} = 19.6$$

Interaction: N $\times$ K

$$= \frac{44^2 + 69^2 + 5^2 + 47^2 + 81^2 + 106^2}{15} - \text{C.F.} -$$

$$(1,505.0 + 19.6)$$

$$= 80.9$$

These sums of squares tally exactly with those already evaluated for the same factors in the original analysis of variance given in Table 72. It is not possible to use the same technique to evaluate factors in the analysis of variance dependent on the distribution of the treatment totals between the three seasons. For example, the season sum of squares is not

$$\frac{18^2 + 29^2 + 115^2}{30} - \text{C.F.},$$

as the three totals used represent values around different assumed means. It is best to evaluate this sum of squares from the season totals given in Table 71 or, alternatively, to compute the actual treatment season totals from Table 73

1933 season total = 6 × 260 − 18 = 1,542
1934 season total = 6 × 470 + 29 = 2,849
1935 season total = 6 × 320 + 115 = 2,035
Grand total..................... 6,426

$$\text{Season S.S.} = \frac{1{,}542^2 + 2{,}849^2 + 2{,}035^2}{30} - \frac{6{,}426^2}{90} = 29{,}043.3$$

Interactions.—The treatment × season interactions may be computed directly from the data of Table 73. For example,

Interaction: season × K
= total season × potash effect − (S.S. season + S.S. potash)

But

Total season × potash S.S. = season S.S. + within-season
potash S.S. (aggregate of three seasons)

Therefore,

Interaction: season × K
= aggregate within-season potash S.S.—S.S. potash

The potash sum of squares has already been computed, and the first term can be evaluated from Table 73, as follows:

Within-season Potash S.S.

$$\text{S.S. K, 1933 season} = \frac{9^2 + 9^2}{15} - \frac{18^2}{30} = 0$$

$$\text{S.S. K, 1934 season} = \frac{3^2 + 26^2}{15} - \frac{29^2}{30} = 17.6$$

$$\text{S.S. K, 1935 season} = \frac{48^2 + 67^2}{15} - \frac{115^2}{30} = 12.0$$

Aggregate within-season potash S.S. = 29.6

Interaction; season × potash = 29.6 − 19.6
= 10.0 (as originally calculated)

In the same way the season × nitrogen interaction may be calculated.

Within-season nitrogen S.S.

$$\text{S.S. N, 1933 season} = \frac{15^2 + 5^2 + 2^2}{10} - \frac{18^2}{30} = \quad 14.6$$

$$\text{S.S. N, 1934 season} = \frac{35^2 + 16^2 + 48^2}{10} - \frac{29^2}{30} = \quad 350.4$$

$$\text{S.S. N, 1935 season} = \frac{63^2 + 41^2 + 137^2}{10} - \frac{115^2}{30} = 2{,}001.1$$

Aggregate within-season nitrogen S.S. $= 2{,}366.1$

Interaction; season $\times$ N $= 2{,}366.1 - 1{,}505.0 = 861.1$

Similarly, the second-order interaction, N $\times$ K $\times$ season, may be calculated by subtracting the total of all the *treatment components* of the analysis of variance from the aggregate within-season treatment sum of squares which, on calculation, will be found to be 2,699.9.

Interaction; N $\times$ K $\times$ season
$\quad = 2{,}699.9 - (1{,}505.0 + 19.6 + 80.9 + 861.1 + 10.0) = 223.3$

This use of several assumed mean values in a single analysis of variance is not limited to data from perennial crops but may be adopted with advantage in many complex experiments in which the data can be allocated to certain distinct groups showing a wide range of values. It is particularly useful in the final calculation of serial experiments, as it makes it possible to use the assumed-mean method in the analysis of each year's data independently and then to combine all the accumulated data into a single comprehensive analysis of variance with the minimum amount of recalculation.

CHAPTER IX

RECENT DEVELOPMENTS IN FIELD EXPERIMENTATION

COMPLEX EXPERIMENTS

The tendency in field experiments today is toward somewhat complicated designs in which several problems are investigated in a single large-scale experiment. The advantages to be derived from the analysis of relatively complex data covering an extensive field of research have already been discussed at the end of Chap. II. In agricultural research, the number of different problems requiring attention is practically unlimited, and the utility of complex field experiments will largely depend on the careful selection of suitable combinations of treatment series. To facilitate the statistical calculations and ensure a valid interpretation of the data, it is often of advantage to adopt a factorial design in which several treatment series occur in all possible combinations; this should preclude an unbalanced or nonorthogonal layout. For example, in an experiment in which two varieties A and B and three fertilizers X, Y, Z are to be tested, the treatments would be six in numbers, *viz.*, AX, AY, AZ, BX, BY, and BZ, each one being replicated n times and located in the field in accordance with any of the standard plot designs. This arrangement does not necessarily mean that the treatments in the experiment have to be limited to those embraced by the factorial scheme. In a randomized block layout, additional treatments entirely separate from the factorial series may be validly included. The analysis of variance of the treatments within the factorial scheme would not be affected by the extra treatments, except in so far as the increased number of plots in a block makes for inefficient control of the soil heterogeneity factor. The secondary treatment comparisons should be dissociated, in the analysis of variance, from those in the factorial scheme, and the type of factor selected should be independent of those in the primary treatment series. The more complex the design, the greater the need to prepare a skeleton analysis of variance before starting work in the field. A preliminary analysis of this nature should show whether the proposed plan is likely to provide a satisfactory answer to the various problems in their correct order of importance.

The analyses of complex experiments are again merely specialized examples of the analysis of variance. It is not possible to quote a standard form which will be truly representative of all types. Each experiment will have to be considered on its own merits. The succeeding two examples should illustrate the various components requiring evaluation in the statistical treatment and should demonstrate how the complex layout does tend to enhance the results.

Example 35. Analysis of a Fodder Grass Experiment in Which Treatments Comprised Four Cutting Rotations and Three Varieties of Grass in All Combinations Giving 4 × 3 Possible Treatment Types.—The layout was on the randomized block principle with four blocks of 12 plots each. The treatment series were as follows:

	Rotations	Varieties
A	Cropped every 45 days or 8 times per year	Elephant grass
B	Cropped every 90 days or 4 times per year	Guatemala grass
C	Cropped every 120 days or 3 times per year	Uba cane
D	Cropped every 160 days or 2 times per year	

TABLE 74.—YIELD FOR FIRST YEAR IN LB. OF DRY MATTER PER $\frac{1}{57}$-ACRE PLOT

Blocks	Elephant grass				Guatemala grass				Uba cane				Block total	Rotation total
	A	*B*	*C*	*D*	*A*	*B*	*C*	*D*	*A*	*B*	*C*	*D*		
I	96	187	222	109	146	252	246	277	115	298	220	430	2,598	*A* = 1,397
II	70	163	125	97	133	181	263	293	143	220	341	371	2,400	*B* = 2,582
III	77	143	134	133	154	224	194	260	117	234	258	484	2,412	*C* = 2,663
IV	80	179	173	113	146	248	190	325	120	253	297	460	2,584	*D* = 3,352
	323	672	654	452	579	905	893	1,155	495	1,005	1,116	1,745	9,994	
Treatment total........	2,101				3,532				4,361				Grand total	

TABLE 75.—ANALYSIS OF VARIANCE

Factor	S.S.	Degrees of freedom	Variance
Total	460,970	47	
Blocks	2,866	3	955
Varieties	163,388	2	81,694**
Rotations	164,650	3	54,883**
Interaction:			
Variety × rotation	95,929	6	15,988**
Error	34,137	33	1,034

423,967 (Total treatment) S.S.

** Significant at the 1 per cent point.

The treatment variances are all obviously significant. An effective method of summarizing results is to draw up a two-way table showing the various treatment means which the analysis of variance has indicated as being significantly different. In large-scale factorial experiments several separate tables of this type may be required. They should preferably be recorded in the recognized commercial units, and the appropriate standard errors should be entered. The numerical value of the standard error depends on the number of plots associated with the treatment mean to which it refers. Separate standard errors will generally have to be evaluated for the two types of main effects tabulated in the marginal entries and for the entries in the center of the table from which the interaction variance has been derived.

TABLE 76.—MEAN YIELDS OF DRY MATTER IN TONS PER ACRE

	Cutting rotation				Varietal mean
	A	B	C	D	
Elephant grass	2.05	4.27	4.17	2.88	3.34 ± 0.167
		± .335			
Guatemala grass	3.69	5.75	5.68	7.34	5.62 ± 0.167
Uba cane	3.15	6.39	7.10	11.10	6.93 ± 0.167
Rotation mean	2.96	5.47	5.65	7.11	

± .236

The appropriate two-way table for this fodder grass experiment is appended.

Using three times the standard error as the critical difference, it is obvious from the right-hand marginal entries that the varieties can be arranged in the following order of merit on the average result of four different cutting rotations:

   a. Uba cane
   b. Guatemala grass
   c. Elephant grass

The rotation means show that the 90- and 120-day series (*B* and *C*) are intermediate in yield potentiality between *A*, the short rotation of 45 days, and *D*, the long one of 180 days.   Series *D* has given much the highest yield of dry matter per acre, as assessed from the average or aggregate response from all three varieties of fodder grass.   In contrast to this general effect, the significant interaction shows that with the elephant grass there is a significant drop in yield from the *C* to *D* series, while with the two other varieties there is a significant rise which is particularly marked in the case of the Uba cane variety.   The difference in the length of the cutting rotation between the *B* and *C* series has not caused any significant alteration in the mean yield for any of the three varieties.   For each of the grasses separately, a 90- to 120-day cutting rotation produces a significant increase in yield over the 45-day rotation, *i.e.*, Series *B* and *C* are better than Series *A*.

This completes the summary of results.   Any of the conclusions noted may be immediately verified by reference to the two-way table of mean values.   In writing up experimental results, tables showing the significant treatment mean values with the appropriate standard errors are the only ones essential to an effective presentation of the data and conclusions.   In more complex experiments it might also be advisable to include the analysis of variance table as the simplest method of demonstrating the experimental design, the nature of the error variance, and the response of the nonsignificant treatment series.   For future reference, the actual yield data might sometimes be included as an appendix.

SPLIT-PLOT EXPERIMENT

In an experiment of the complex type, it is often advantageous to use a standard field arrangement with relatively large plots for one series of treatments. By subdivision of these whole plots into so many similar subplots, a second series of treatments may be superimposed on the first. The number of subplots in each whole plot should be made equal to the number of treatments in the second series, and each of these treatments should occur once and once only in each whole plot, the allocation over the subplots being a random one. This will ensure a balanced layout covering all possible combinations of the treatments in the two series and permitting of a straightforward and valid statistical interpretation of the results. For certain types of experiment this split-plot design may greatly simplify the field practice. For example, in comparing different depths of ploughing, relatively large plots are practically a necessity if the ploughs are to do accurate work. Similarly, treatments that have to be harvested on different dates are much more accessible, if a reasonably large plot can be cut at one time.

In contrast to the complete randomization of treatment types as described in the previous example, the split-plot system provides a more critical comparison of the subplot treatments but a less critical comparison of the whole-plot units. One reason is that the number of replications and consequently, the number of degrees of freedom pertaining to the estimate of error is much greater in the former than in the latter. Furthermore, the large size of the whole plot gives less efficient control over soil heterogeneity. It is for this reason that, in a split-plot experiment, a Latin-square arrangement of the whole plots is definitely preferable to a randomized block layout. In any case, the less important treatment comparisons should be allocated to the whole plots, and the treatment series for which a really critical test is desired should be located in the subplots. Alternatively, in experiments in which all the treatment comparisons are of equal importance, the whole plots should be used for those likely to show relatively large treatment differences.

Just as in perennial crops, a number of successive harvests does not increase the number of degrees of freedom upon which the estimate of error of the aggregate plot yield is based, so the subdivision of the whole plots does not entail any multiplication of the whole-plot replications. Where subdivision of the whole plots is practiced, the correct type of analysis is the one involving two estimates of error, (*a*) and (*b*). In working out the analysis of variance, it is best to express all the values in the smallest units or subplots to which the whole plots have been subdivided.

Example 36. Statistical Analysis of Data from a Complex Cotton Experiment* in Which Certain Treatments Appear in Subplot Units.—In this experiment, four sowing dates, three spacings, three rates of irrigation, and two rates of nitrogenous manuring were superimposed in all combinations giving $4 \times 3 \times 3 \times 2$ or 72 different treatment types. The individual treatments in each series were as follows:

Sowing date	Spacing	Irrigation	Fertilizer
I. July 24.....	(*a*) 25 cm. between holes	*x* Light	(0) Control
II. August 11...	(*b*) 50 cm. between holes	*y* Medium	(N) Sulphate of
III. Sept. 2......	(*c*) 75 cm. between holes	*z* Heavy	ammonia at rate
IV. Sept 25.....			of 600 rotls per
			feddan

The layout consisted of four blocks, each containing four large whole plots to accommodate the four different dates of sowing on a random arrangement within each block. Every whole plot was subdivided into nine subplots to take all combinations (3×3) of the spacing and irrigation series, again located at random over the subplots in each whole plot. Each of the 144 subplots was in turn subdivided into two half subplots, one-half of each pair being given a nitrogenous fertilizer and the other half being used as a control. There were therefore in the experiment 16 whole plots, 144 subplots, and 288 half subplots, entailing in the analysis of variance three separate estimates of error, each one applicable to its own particular treatment comparisons. Each of these three sections can be regarded as an independent experiment and analyzed on the randomized block principle. For example, for the subplot treatments, the 16 whole plots are exactly equivalent to 16 randomized blocks. As already noted,

* *J. Agr. Sci.*, 22: 616.

TABLE 77.—YIELD OF SEED COTTON IN KANTARS PER FEDDAN

Duty of water	Spacing, cm.	Date of sowing												Total
		I. July 24			II. Aug. 11			III. Sept. 2			IV. Sept. 25			
		0	N	Sub-plot total	0	N	Sub-plot total	0	N	Sub-plot total	0	N	Sub-plot total	
x Light	(a) 25	9.9	21.5	31.4	16.4	27.5	43.9	19.6	27.9	47.5	15.1	19.9	35.0	157.8
	(b) 50	13.4	21.4	34.8	17.2	26.7	43.9	18.5	23.5	42.0	13.0	13.6	26.6	147.3
	(c) 75	12.6	21.3	33.9	18.0	25.4	43.4	14.0	19.4	33.4	11.6	11.3	22.9	133.6
	Total	35.9	64.2	100.1	51.6	79.6	131.2	52.1	70.8	122.9	39.7	44.8	84.5	438.7
y Medium	(a) 25	14.4	30.1	44.5	17.9	31.9	49.8	18.2	34.8	53.0	16.0	22.7	38.7	186.0
	(b) 50	14.0	28.7	42.7	21.2	30.8	52.0	18.9	25.7	44.6	16.1	18.1	34.2	173.5
	(c) 75	13.6	27.1	40.7	19.2	30.9	50.1	18.3	22.7	41.0	11.6	13.9	25.5	157.3
	Total	42.0	85.9	127.9	58.3	93.6	151.9	55.4	83.2	138.6	43.7	54.7	98.4	516.8
z Heavy	(a) 25	12.3	33.3	45.6	18.5	35.8	54.3	19.8	34.9	54.7	18.3	24.3	42.6	197.2
	(b) 50	12.8	33.6	46.4	20.6	32.3	52.9	18.2	30.0	48.2	14.1	19.1	33.2	180.7
	(c) 75	15.6	32.6	48.2	21.0	35.6	56.6	16.3	20.9	37.2	12.7	13.3	26.0	168.0
	Total	40.7	99.5	140.2	60.1	103.7	163.8	54.3	85.8	140.1	45.1	56.7	101.8	545.9
	Grand total	118.6	249.6	368.2	170.0	276.9	446.9	161.8	239.8	401.6	128.5	156.2	284.7	1,501.4

Fertilizer total   Spacing total

(0) Control = 578.9   (a) 25 cm. = 541.0

(N) Sulphate = 922.5   (b) 50 cm. = 501.5

                       (c) 75 cm. = 458.9

it is better to work throughout in the smallest plot units and to draw up, in a single table, a composite analysis for the whole data.   This makes it possible to assess first-, second-, and third-order treatment interactions and to derive the full benefit from the complex layout.

To reduce Table 77 to a reasonable size, only the mean yield per half subplot for each of the 72 different treatment types has been recorded.   Each of these yields represents the mean of the four replicates from the four large blocks included in the experiment.   This fact must be remembered in using Table 77 to work out the analysis of variance.

TABLE 78.—ANALYSIS OF VARIANCE

Factor	S.S.	Degrees of freedom	Variance
Total whole plot........................	*4,531*	*15*	
Blocks.............................	1,000†	3	
Sowing date........................	3,129	3	1,043.0**
Error (*a*)...........................	402	9	44.7
Total subplot........................	*7,609*	*143*	
Whole plot, *i.e.*, the subplot blocks......	4,531	15	
Spacing............................	562	2	281.0**
Irrigation..........................	1,022	2	511.0.
Interactions: Spacing × irrigation.......	7	4	1.8
Sowing date × spacing..............	660	6	110.0**
Sowing date × irrigation.............	134	6	22.3**
Sowing × spacing × irrigation........	103	12	8.3
Error (*b*)...........................	590	96	6.15
Total half subplots......................	*16,996*	*287*	
Subplots, *i.e.*, the half subplot blocks....	7,609	143	
Nitrogen............................	6,559	1	6,559.0**
Interactions: N × sowing date..........	1,316	3	438.7**
N × spacing......................	305	2	152.5**
N × irrigation....................	360	2	180.0**
N × spacing × irrigation............	27	4	6.8
N × sowing × irrigation.............	108	6	18.0**
N × sowing × spacing..............	74	6	12.3*
N × sowing × spacing × irrigation...	86	12	7.2
Error (*c*)...........................	552	108	5.11

† This value is merely an arbitrary one put in to complete the analysis.   It cannot be calculated from the data in Table 77.

* Significant at 5 per cent point.

** Significant at 1 per cent point.

As an illustration of the way in which the components of the analysis of variance have been obtained, the calculation of a few of them is appended.

S.S. sowing date

$$= \left[\frac{(368.2^2 + 446.9^2 + 401.6^2 + 284.7^2)}{72} - \frac{(1,501.4)^2}{288} \right] \times 16\dagger\dagger$$

$$= 3,129$$

$$S.S.\ nitrogen = \frac{(922.5 - 578.9)^2 \times 16\dagger\dagger}{288} = 6,559$$

Interaction; nitrogen $\times$ sowing date.

Aggregate nitrogen and sowing date S.S.

$$= \left[\frac{(118.6^2 + 249.6^2 + 170.0^2 + \cdots 128.5^2 + 156.2^2)}{36} - \frac{(1,501.4)^2}{288} \right] \times 16\dagger\dagger$$

$$= 11,004$$

Interaction,

$$\text{nitrogen} \times \text{sowing date} = 11,004 - (6,559 + 3,129)$$
$$= 1,316$$

Alternatively, this interaction can be calculated directly from the differences between comparable totals.

I + II with N	= 526.5		III + IV with N	= 396.0
I + II with 0	= 288.6		III + IV with 0	= 290.3
Difference D_1	= 237.9		D_2	= 105.7
I + IV with N	= 405.8		II + III with N	= 516.7
I + IV with 0	= 247.1		II + III with 0	= 331.8
D_3	= 158.7		D_4	= 184.9
I + III with N	= 489.4		II + IV with N	= 433.1
I + III with 0	= 280.4		II + IV with 0	= 298.5
D_5	= 209.0		D_6	= 134.6

$$D_1 - D_2 = \quad 132.2$$
$$D_3 - D_4 = -\ 26.2$$
$$D_5 - D_6 = \quad 74.4$$

S.S. interaction, nitrogen $\times$ sowing date =

$$\frac{(132.2^2 + 26.2^2 + 74.4^2) \times 16\dagger\dagger}{288} = 1,316$$

$\dagger\dagger$ This factor is necessary to compensate for data tabulated as mean values of four replicates.

A similar technique might be used to calculate the higher order interactions, but where a number of factors are involved, it is simpler to use the former method in which the aggregate sum of squares for the factors separately is subtracted from the total treatment sum of squares for all combinations of the factors.

Thus, S.S. interaction, sowing date $\times$ spacing $\times$ irrigation $=$

$$\left[\frac{31.4^2 + 34.8^2 + \cdots 33.2^2 + 26.0^2}{8} - \frac{1,501.4^2}{288} \right] \times 16 -$$
$$(3,129 + 562 + 1,022 + 7 + 660 + 134) = 103$$

The following résumé of the chief results has been taken verbatim from the original article.

Yield both with and without nitrogen application has optional value for August sowing.

The returns in yield for nitrogen application decline with advancing sowing date.

Spacing has little effect with early sowing but has large effect with late sowing, irrespective of nitrogen application.

Water supply with early sowing and nitrogen application has large effect.

Water supply with early sowing without nitrogen has little effect.

The effect of water supply tends to disappear with advancing sowing date irrespective of nitrogen application. Various combinations of factors may be utilised to give maximal yield, thus giving considerable latitude in sowing date without sacrifice of yield. The inter-relations of the factors studied indicate the limits between which, by suitable practice, the yield of cotton may be improved or controlled.

The results are therefore both comprehensive and conclusive and bear witness to the advantages of complex experimentation where both the field and laboratory control is sufficiently skilled.

ANALYSIS OF COVARIANCE IN FIELD EXPERIMENTS

One of the chief difficulties in obtaining conclusive results from field trials is the impossibility of finding even approximately uniform plots. No matter how technically perfect the design of an experiment may be, there will still remain very definite differences from plot to plot in soil and environmental fertility, in germination, in disease and pest incidence, and in the ultimate plant population from which the yield data are recorded. Modern methods of layout have greatly reduced the effects of this heterogeneity on the final interpretation of the results. Even today, however, in experiments in which the general design and execution are beyond reproach, the plot variation is often sufficiently great to mask certain real differences between the treatments under comparison. In many experiments this plot variation is obviously correlated with certain external factors as plant population, soil fertility, age of the crop, number of tillers, etc. When a fair estimate of the coefficient of correlation between the yield data and the particular external factor influencing results can be computed, it may be possible to use this information to produce a valid reduction in the estimate of experimental error and to demonstrate real treatment differences that would otherwise have been swamped in plot variability. For example, preliminary uniformity trials might be used to assess the fertility values of certain plots required for subsequent experiments. On the assumption that these values do not change greatly for the succeeding experimental crop, by the analysis of covariance it is possible to use the data from the uniformity trial to adjust the yields in the experiment so as to compensate for soil fertility differences between the plots. A valid statistical comparison of the corrected treatment yields can then be carried out and an accurate estimate of their respective merits obtained. Similarly, many experiments are spoiled because, owing to uncontrollable environmental factors, the plant population is far from uniform. It is often possible to make a count of the number of plants per plot and to use this to correct the yields for population. It is not sufficient merely to divide the yield by the plant number, as, of course, widely spaced plants develop very differently from closely spaced ones and results based directly on the yield per plant would be biased in favor of the thinly populated treatments. The statistical treatment depends on the use of the regression coefficient to determine the average yield that might be expected for any given number of plants and on the dispersion of the treatment means relative to this linear regression. In the following examples, it is assumed that the reader is familiar with the elementary facts relative to the calculation and significance of the coefficient of regression and to its application in a simple analysis of covariance as detailed in Chap. VI.

Example 37. Analysis of Covariance Applied to a Cotton Varietal Test.—In the following small experiment, five rows of each of three selected varieties of cotton were sown. The rows were arranged on the randomized block principle. The quantity of seed of each variety available was limited, so that it was impossible to equalize the plant number per row and make up for deficiencies in germination, mortality incidence, etc. A count of the number of plants per row surviving at harvest was accordingly taken, and the results are appended.

TABLE 79.—POPULATION NUMBER AND YIELD OF COTTON LINT IN OUNCES
PER ROW

Variety	(x) Yield of lint, oz. per row						
	Number of block					Variety total	Variety mean
	I	II	III	IV	V		
A	11	8	9	6	5	39	7.8
B	5	6	10	8	4	33	6.6
C	4	7	6	3	4	24	4.8
Row or block total..........	20	21	25	17	13	Grand total 96	

Variety	(y) No. of plants per row						
	Number of block					Variety total	Variety mean
	I	II	III	IV	V		
A	16	12	13	10	8	59	11.8
B	12	14	18	15	10	69	13.8
C	7	13	10	7	6	43	8.6
Row or block total..........	35	39	41	32	24	Grand total 171	

Consider first the x analysis of variance of the yield data alone. The variances for variety and error are, respectively, 11.4 and 3.74, giving a calculated value of $F = 3.05$. The corresponding reading from the Table of F at the 5 per cent level is 4.46, proving that, for the yield data alone, there is no significant difference between the three varieties. There is, however, considerable variation in the number of plants per plot, which

TABLE 80.—ANALYSIS OF VARIANCE AND COVARIANCE

	Analysis of x			Analysis of y			Analysis of xy	
	C.F. by variable-squared method $= \dfrac{96^2}{15} = 614.4$			C.F. by variable-squared method $= \dfrac{171^2}{15} = 1{,}949.4$			C.F. $= \dfrac{96 \times 171}{15} = 1{,}094.4$	
x^2	Square of block total	Square of variety total	y^2	Square of block total	Square of variety total	xy	xy for block total	xy for variety total
121	400	1,521	256	1,225	3,481	176	700	2,301
25	441	1,089	144	1,521	4,761	60	819	2,277
16	625	576	49	1,681	1,849	28	1,025	1,032
64	289	5)3,186	144	1,024	5)10,091	96	544	5)5,610
36	169	637.2	196	576	2,018.2	84	312	1,122
49	3)1,924	−614.4	169	3)6,027	−1,949.4	91	3)3,400	−1,094.4
81	641.3	22.8 = variety S.S.	169	2,009	68.8 = variety S.S.	117	1,133.3	+27.6 = variety S.P.
100	−614.4		324	−1,949.4		180	−1,094.4	
36	26.9 = block S.S.		100	59.6 = block S.S.		60	+38.9 = block S.P.	
64			100			120		
9			225			21		
25			49			40		
16			64			40		
16			100			24		
694			36			1,197		
−614.4			2,125			−1,094.4		
79.6 = total S.S.			−1,949.4			+102.6 = total S.P.		
			175.6 = total S.S.					

Factor	Degrees of freedom	S.S. x	S.S. y	S.P. xy
Total...........	14	79.6	175.6	102.4
Blocks.........	4	26.9	59.6	38.9
Variety........	2	22.8	68.8	27.6
Error..........	8	29.9	47.2	36.1

presumably is partly responsible for the high estimate of the error of x. It is proposed therefore, to carry out an analysis of covariance, so as to determine whether the varieties are significantly different when the mean yields are adjusted on a basis equalizing the number of plants per plot. The first step is to calculate the coefficient of regression of yield on plant number, and verify that it is significant. The best estimate of the coefficient of regression comes from the error line of the analysis given in Table 78, *i.e.*, after the variety and block effects have been eliminated.

$$b_{xy} = \frac{\text{S.P. } xy}{\text{S.S. } y} = \frac{36.1}{47.2} = 0.7648$$

The significance of b_{xy} may be determined by calculating the standard error and comparing the calculated value of t with the appropriate reading from the Table of t. Here, the alternative method by splitting up the error variance of x to its two components—the linear regression and deviations from this regression—and reference to the Table of F is probably easier.

$$\text{Linear regression S.S.} = \frac{(\text{S.P. } xy)^2}{\text{S.S. } y}$$

$$= \frac{36.1^2}{47.2} = 27.6 \text{ with 1 degree of freedom}$$

S.S. deviations from regression $= 29.9 - 27.6 = 2.3$ with
7 degrees of freedom

$$F = \frac{27.6}{2.3/7} = 83.6$$

The reading from the table for $n_1 = 1$, $n_2 = 7$, and $P = 0.01$ is only 12.25, proving that the coefficient of regression of yield on plant number is highly significant. The analysis of the reduced variance may now be validly applied to adjust the yield data for variation in plant number and increase the accuracy of the statistical evaluation. This final analysis is limited to the treatment and error components, as it may fairly be assumed that the block effects have already been taken out in the original analysis of Table 80. The procedure then becomes identical with that already given in Table 52 (Chap. VI).

TABLE 81.—ANALYSIS OF REDUCED VARIANCE

Factor	S.S. x	S.S. y	S.P. xy	$\Sigma(x - X)^2$	Degrees of freedom	Reduced variance
Variety.......	22.8	68.8	27.6	11.73	1	11.73
Error........	29.9	47.2	36.1	2.29	7	0.33
Total (variety + error)....	52.7	116.0	63.7	17.73	9	
Residual $\Sigma(x - X)^2 =$				3.71	1	3.71

The F test shows that the residual variance compared with that of error is significant on a probability approaching 0.01. This proves that there is a significant difference between the variety means corrected for plant number. The corrected mean values must now be calculated from $x_t - b_{xy}(y_t - M_y)$, the notation being that previously used in Chap. VI. In this example, b_{xy} is 0.7648, as already calculated.

TABLE 82.—TABLE OF YIELDS CORRECTED FOR PLANT NUMBER

Variety	Mean no. of plants (y_t)	$(y_t - M_y)$ $[M_y = 11.4]$	$b_{xy}(y_t - M_y)$	Mean yield (x_t)	Corrected yield
A	11.8	+0.4	+0.306	7.8	7.49
B	13.8	+2.4	+1.835	6.6	4.77
C	8.6	−2.8	−2.141	4.8	6.94

The standard error of the difference D between any pair of these corrected mean yields $= \sqrt{E\left(\dfrac{2}{n} + \dfrac{D_y^2}{\text{S.S. } y \text{ for error}}\right)}$

where $E =$ error variance of $\Sigma(x - X)^2$.

$n =$ number of plots from which each mean is calculated.

$D_y =$ difference between the corresponding pair of means for plant number.

$$\text{Standard error } A - B = \sqrt{0.33\left(\frac{2}{5} + \frac{2.0^2}{47.2}\right)} = 0.40$$

$$t \text{ (by calculation)} = \frac{D}{E_D} = \frac{2.72}{0.40} = 6.80$$

Reference to the Table of t for $n = 7$ (the degrees of freedom of the reduced error variance) shows this value to be significant on a probability less than 0.01, proving that variety A is a better yielder than B when allowance is made for differences in plant population.

Testing now, $A - C$;

$$t = \frac{0.55}{\sqrt{0.33\left(\frac{2}{5} + \frac{3.2^2}{47.2}\right)}} = 1.21$$

and for $C - B$;

$$t = \frac{2.17}{\sqrt{0.33\left(\frac{2}{5} + \frac{5.2^2}{47.2}\right)}} = 3.81$$

For 7 degrees of freedom, the first of these two values of t is nonsignificant, and the second is significant on a probability approaching 0.01.

In conclusion, therefore, it can be stated that when conditions are equalized as regards the population factor both the A and the C varieties are markedly superior in yield to B. This is a strikingly different result from that obtained from a straightforward analysis of variance of the yield data alone. Not only is a negative result changed into a positive one, but the relative position of the three varieties is very different from what might be anticipated from the actual mean varietal yields (Table 82).

It is possibly of interest to show how the expression for the standard error has been derived. D represents the difference between the actual mean yields of the two varieties less b_{xy} $\times$ the difference between the corresponding pair of means for plant number. The first part of the standard error $\frac{2E}{n}$ is the variance of the first component of D, and the second part $\frac{D_y^2 \times E}{\text{S.S. } y}$ the variance of the second component. The standard error of the difference between these two components is therefore equivalent to the square root of the sum of these two variances, $i.e.$, the standard error of D is given by the formula quoted.

UNIFORMITY TRIAL AS A CONTROL OF PLOT VARIATION

With orchard and perennial crops in general, genetical heterogeneity, seasonal fluctuations, age differences, the limited number of individuals on each plot, and the unavoidable extensive acreage of any large-scale experiment, all combine to make the uncontrollable variability between units an even more serious hindrance to successful yield trials than in the case of annual

TABLE 83.—YIELD OF CANE IN HUNDREDWEIGHTS PER $\frac{1}{20}$-ACRE PLOT

Blocks	Ratoon crop (x)					Plant cane (y)				
	Manures				Block total	Manures				Block total
	O	M	I	MI		O	M	I	MI	
I	25	33	40	43	141	45	51	38	48	182
II	16	30	43	57	146	27	49	40	61	177
III	25	22	39	29	115	42	36	42	33	153
IV	30	52	34	53	169	53	70	31	59	213
V	37	51	25	28	141	71	74	21	31	197
Treatment total......	133	188	181	210	Grand total 712	238	280	172	232	Grand total 922
Treatment mean.....	26.6	37.6	36.2	42.0	General mean 35.6	47.6	56.0	34.4	46.4	General mean 46.1

crops. With perennials, preliminary uniformity trials as a means of estimating the relative fertility values of the ultimate experimental units may often be utilized to considerable advantage. The above data from a manurial experiment with sugar cane provide an excellent illustration of this, the plant cane crop being used to measure the potential fertility of the plots and the mean yields of the various treatments given to the ratoon crop being adjusted accordingly. The fertilizers applied were farmyard manure and a complete artificial in all combinations of the two rates of dressings 0 and 1, resulting in the following four treatments:.

O = control: no fertilizer applied.

M = farmyard manure at the rate of 20 tons per acre.

I = complete inorganic fertilizer at the rate of 90 pounds N, 375 pounds P_2O_5, and 50 pounds K_2O per acre.

MI = combined farmyard and inorganic fertilizers at the rates quoted above.

The yield of cane for the two crops in hundredweights per $\frac{1}{20}$-acre plot and the analyses of variance and covariance are appended.

The analysis of variance of x was first used to test whether there was any significant difference between the treatment means of the experimental crop. The biggest treatment variance

TABLE 84.—ANALYSIS OF VARIANCE AND COVARIANCE

Factor	Degrees of freedom	Analysis of variance of x		Analysis of variance of y		Analysis of covariance, xy	
		S.S.	Mean square	S.S.	Mean square	S.P.	Mean S.P.
Total..................	19	2,488.8		4,303.8		+ 2,095.8	
Blocks.................	4	368.8		505.8		395.0	
Treatments:							
Farmyard manure.......	1	352.8	352.8	520.2†	520.2	428.4	428.4
Inorganics.............	1	245.0	245.0	649.8†	649.8	399.0	399.0
Interaction $I \times M$.......	1	33.8	33.8	16.2†	16.2	23.4	23.4
Error..................	12	1,488.4	124.0	2,611.8	217.7	1,694.8	141.2

† For the plant cane crop, the grouping into treatments is, of course, imaginary, but it is better to carry out the analysis so as to develop parallel series for x, y, and xy.

is that for the response to farmyard manure. This gives a calculated value of z of 0.5227 as compared with the reading from the Table of z (for $n_1 = 1$, and $n_2 = 12$, and $P = 0.05$) of 0.7788. The treatment means must therefore be regarded as not significantly different even though the mean values show considerable variation, especially when the no manure treatment is compared with the others. The explanation of this apparently lies in the relatively high error variance as a consequence of the large variation between the yields of similar plots. It was therefore decided to use the regression of x on y, $i.e.$, of the ratoon crop yields corrected in accordance with the yields recorded in the uniformity trial or plant cane crop. The first step is, of course, to test the significance of the regression coefficient.

$$b_{xy} \text{ (from error variance)} = \frac{+1,694.8}{2,611.8} = +0.649$$

$$\text{Standard error of } b_{xy} = \sqrt{\frac{1,488.4 - 0.649^2 \times 2,611.8}{11 \times 2,611.8}}$$

$$= 0.117 \text{ (11 degrees of freedom)}$$

$$t \text{ (by calculation)} = \frac{0.649}{0.117} = 5.54$$

which corresponds to a probability considerably less than 0.01. Therefore, after due allowance has been made for treatment and block effects, there is a marked positive correlation between the yields of the individual plots in the ratoon and plant cane crops. It is now permissible to use the $(x - X)^2$ analysis to determine any significant differences between the various treatments.

Where the treatments are complex, as in this experiment, it is advisable to carry out the $(x - X)^2$ analysis for each type of comparison and interaction separately.

TABLE 85.—ANALYSIS OF REDUCED VARIANCE FOR FARMYARD MANURE—
MAIN EFFECT

Factor	S.S. x	S.S. y	S.P. xy	$\Sigma(x - X)^2$	Degrees of freedom $\Sigma(x - X)^2$	Variance
Farmyard manure	352.8	520.2	428.4	0	0	
Error............	1,488.4	2,611.8	1,694.8	388.4	11	35.3
Total..........	1,841.2	3,132.0	2,123.2	402.2	12	
Residual.....				13.8	1	13.8

The reduced variances for the residual and error components are not significantly different, proving that there is no apparent response to the dressing of farmyard manure, even when the data from the uniformity trial are used to provide an equalized estimate of the treatment means. As already explained in Chap. VI, with only two treatments, the reduced variance for the first line of the above table is bound to be zero and need not be calculated.

F (Table 86) is 23.55, a value which is significant on a probability less than 0.01. The error variance can therefore be used to compare the corrected mean values for the 10 plots with and the 10 plots without inorganics.

TABLE 86.—ANALYSIS OF REDUCED VARIANCE FOR INORGANIC MANURES—
MAIN EFFECT

Factor	S.S. x	S.S. y	S.P. xy	$\Sigma(x - X)^2$	Degrees of freedom	Mean square
Inorganics	245.0	649.8	399.0			
Error	1,488.4	2,611.8	1,694.8	388.4	11	35.3
Total	1,733.4	3,261.6	1,295.0	1,219.7		
Residual				831.3	1	831.3

TABLE 87

Treatment	x_t	$b_{xy}(y_t - M_y)$	Corrected yield
No inorganics	32.1	0.649(51.8 − 46.1)	28.4
With inorganics	39.1	0.649(40.4 − 46.1)	42.8
Difference			14.4

Standard error of difference between corrected yields

$$= \sqrt{35.3\left(\frac{2}{10} + \frac{11.4^2}{2,611.8}\right)}$$
$$= 2.97$$

$$t \text{ (by calculation)} = \frac{14.4}{2.97} = 4.85 \text{ (11 degrees of freedom)}$$

This value of t is significant on a probability less than 0.01. Actually, as there are only two treatment means involved, the t test is redundant, since it merely represents another method of arriving at exactly the same result as already obtained by calculating F.

A similar analysis for the interaction of $I \times M$ shows it to be nonsignificant. The final conclusion would therefore be that, when the original fertility of the plots is equalized, the application of inorganics to the ratoon crop has produced a significant increase in yield. The use of farmyard manure, alone or in combination with artificial fertilizers is of no benefit toward increasing the yield. Of course, it is possible that the effect of the farmyard manure may not make itself felt till the second ratoon crop, and further yield data would be necessary to test this point.

In this example, therefore, the use of the data from the uniformity trial has changed a negative result into a positive one and has made it possible to select one out of the four alternative dressings tested as being much the best. The actual and corrected mean yields for the four treatments are tabulated below, and they effectively illustrate how this has happened.

Treatment	Mean yield	Corrected mean yield, cwt. per plot
Control: no manure	26.6	25.6
Farmyard manure	37.6	31.2
Inorganic fertilizer	36.2	43.8
Farmyard manure + inorganic fertilizer	42.0	41.8

LINEAR REGRESSION COMPONENT OF THE TREATMENT VARIANCE

In crop experiments the treatments are often quantitative in character and represent different rates of a certain factor on some regular incremental scale, such as zero, single, double, and treble quantities of a certain fertilizer. When this occurs, it is possible to segregate the linear regression component of the treatment variance. This component is a measure of the general effect on the crop of the increasing doses of this particular treatment factor. If the response is sufficiently definite and uniform, the regression and error variances will be significantly different, as determined by evaluating F or z. When the response is regular and the difference between the treatment means is not very great, it is even possible for the regression variance to show significance, when the F test applied to the treatment variance as a whole has given a negative result. The following example effectively illustrates the application of this method to yield data obtained from a manurial experiment with sugar cane.

The reading of z from the table for the 5 per cent distribution is 0.6250, so that on this basis of comparison there is no significant response to the manures applied. Examination of the treatment totals shows a definite increase in yield from the control up to the heaviest dressing of farmyard manure, and the effects of the manures have evidently been swamped by plot variability. As a

TABLE 88.—YIELD OF PLANT CANE IN HALF-HUNDREDWEIGHTS PER ⅟₃₀-ACRE PLOT AROUND AN ASSUMED MEAN OF 40 HALF-CWT.

Blocks	Dressing of farmyard manure, tons per acre								Block total	
	0		10		20		30			
	−	+	−	+	−	+	−	+	−	+
1	12		5		0		7		24	
2	4			2	3			1	4	
3	8			3	3		0		8	
4		1	5			6		7		9
5		6		7		7		9		29
Treatment total..	−17		+2		+7		+10		Grand total +2	

TABLE 89.—ANALYSIS OF VARIANCE OF YIELD DATA

Factor	S.S.	Degrees of freedom	Variance	$\frac{1}{2}\log_e$ of $\frac{\text{variance}}{10}$
Total...............	655.8	19		
Blocks..............	394.3	4		
Treatment..........	88.2	3	29.4	0.5392 ⎱
Error..............	173.3	12	14.4	0.1823 ⎰ $z = 0.3569$

more exact test of the manurial response, it is proposed to calculate the regression of the treatment yields (x) on quantity of manure applied (y), the dressings being taken as 0, 1, 2, and 3 units, and allowance being made for the fact that each treatment total represents five plot yields.

$$\text{S.S. } y = \frac{0^2 + 1^2 + 2^2 + 3^2}{5} - \frac{6^2}{20} = 1$$

$$\text{S.P. } xy = \frac{(0\times-17) + (1\times2) + (2\times7) + (3\times10)}{5} - \frac{6\times2}{20} = 8.6$$

$$\text{S.S. linear regression} = \frac{(\text{S.P. } xy)^2}{\text{S.S. } y} = \frac{8.6^2}{1} = 73.96$$

The reading of z for the 5 per cent distribution is 0.7788. The regression variance is therefore significant, proving that there has been a definite response to the farmyard manure; the heavier the dressing of manure, the greater the yield of cane.

TABLE 90.—DETAILED ANALYSIS

Factor	S.S.	Degrees of freedom		Variance	$\frac{1}{2}\log_e$ of $\frac{\text{variance}}{10}$	
Total.............	655.8	19				
Blocks............	394.3	4				
Linear regression...	73.9	1 ⎱	Treatment S.S.	73.9	1.0001 ⎱	
Deviations........	14.3	2 ⎰		7.1		$z = 0.8178$
Error............	173.3	12		14.4	0.1823 ⎰	

CONFOUNDING OF TREATMENT EFFECTS

At the end of Chap. VII, the need for an orthogonal design in agricultural experiments was emphasized, and it was shown that, when this principle was not observed, it was possible for certain treatment effects to become entangled with one another in a way that considerably complicates the statistical analysis of the data. *Confounding* in field experiments is a term used to define a plot arrangement in which a portion of the less important treatment effects—usually the higher order interactions— is purposely confounded or entangled with that of blocks. It really represents a controlled deviation from the standard experimental designs. Confounding is only practicable in rela- tively complex factorial experiments embracing several different problems concurrently. The technique consists of splitting up each block into so many equal subblocks and allocating the various treatment combinations to those subblocks in a way that ensures that certain unimportant treatment effects are entangled or included in the subblock variance. For any given factorial combination the treatments may be allocated to the subblocks in only a few alternative ways in order to confound any selected treatment effect. Incorrect allocation to the subblocks will result in a nonorthogonal layout, which may completely upset the results. Yates* has enumerated the possible alternative subblock arrangements in order to achieve the confounding of specified treatment effects in certain standard types of experi- ment. One of the simplest forms of experiment in which con- founding is practicable is the one in which there are $2 \times 2 \times 2$ or

* The Design and Analysis of Factorial Experiments, *Imp. Bur. Soil Sci. Tech. Comm.* 35.

2^3 treatment series, *e.g.*, in a trial including two varieties A_1 and A_2, two spacings B_1 and B_2, and two dates of sowing C_1 and C_2. If no confounding was introduced, the number of plots in a block would be eight to cover the eight possible treatment combinations, *viz.*:

$$
\begin{array}{ll}
(1)\ A_2\ B_1\ C_1 & \\
(2)\ A_1\ B_1\ C_2 & \\
(3)\ A_1\ B_2\ C_1 & \text{(Subblock } a) \\
(4)\ A_2\ B_2\ C_2 & \\
\end{array}
$$

$$
\begin{array}{ll}
(5)\ A_1\ B_1\ C_1 & \\
(6)\ A_2\ B_1\ C_2 & \\
(7)\ A_2\ B_2\ C_1 & \text{(Subblock } b) \\
(8)\ A_1\ B_2\ C_2 & \\
\end{array}
$$

If the experiment consisted of four such blocks of eight plots, the skeleton analysis of variance would be as follows:

Factor	Degrees of freedom
Total	31
Blocks	3
Treatments:	
Main Effects: Variety (A)	1 ⎫
Spacing (B)	1 ⎪
Sowing Date (C)	1 ⎪
Interactions: 1st order. $A \times B$	1 ⎬ 7
$A \times C$	1 ⎪
$B \times C$	1 ⎪
2d order. $A \times B \times C$	1 ⎭
Error	21

If, in the same experiment, the blocks were each subdivided to two subblocks of four plots each to take treatments 1 to 4, and 5 to 8, respectively, the second-order interaction, $A \times B \times C$, becomes completely confounded with the subblock sum of squares, and the appropriate analysis would then become as follows:

| | Degrees of |
Factor	freedom
Total	31
Blocks, *i.e.*, subblocks	7
Treatments:	
Main Effects: Variety (A)	1
Spacing (B)	1
Sowing date (C)	1
Interactions: $A \times B$	1
$A \times C$	1
$B \times C$	1
Error	18

The main effects and interactions together account for 6 degrees of freedom.

By a different allocation of the treatments between the pairs of subblocks, it is possible to confound either the $A \times B$, the $B \times C$ or the $A \times C$ first-order interactions with the blocks instead of the second-order one $A \times B \times C$. There would then be 3 degrees of freedom for the main treatment comparisons, two for the unconfounded first-order interactions and one for the second-order interaction.

The alternative groupings are appended.

Factor confounded	Subblock a			Subblock b		
$A \times C$ interaction	A_2	B_1	C_1	A_1	B_1	C_1
	A_1	B_1	C_2	A_1	B_2	C_1
	A_2	B_2	C_1	A_2	B_1	C_2
	A_1	B_2	C_2	A_2	B_2	C_2
$A \times B$ interaction	A_2	B_1	C_1	A_1	B_1	C_1
	A_1	B_2	C_1	A_1	B_1	C_2
	A_2	B_1	C_2	A_2	B_2	C_1
	A_1	B_2	C_2	A_2	B_2	C_2
$B \times C$ interaction	A_1	B_1	C_2	A_1	B_1	C_1
	A_1	B_2	C_1	A_2	B_1	C_1
	A_2	B_1	C_2	A_1	B_2	C_2
	A_2	B_2	C_1	A_2	B_2	C_2

Partial Confounding.—In any 2^3 confounded experiment, it will be necessary to include several replications of each treatment series in order to provide an error variance based on an adequate number of degrees of freedom. In the example cited, there are four replications of each treatment combination, arranged in four pairs of subblocks. In each pair or group of subblocks, each treatment series will occur only once. It is valid and sometimes advantageous to adopt the practice of partial confounding in which the separate subblock groups are used to confound different treatment effects. In a 2^3 confounded experiment with four complete replications or eight subblocks in four pairs, a partial confounded arrangement which gives a nicely balanced design is one in which each type of interaction— $A \times B$, $A \times C$, $B \times C$, $A \times B \times C$—is confounded in a different pair of subblocks. There will then be 1 degree of freedom available for each main effect and each interaction, leaving 17 degrees of freedom for error. In computing any particular interaction for an experiment of this type, the plot yields from the subblock pair with which this interaction is confounded are ignored, and the data from the remaining six subblocks are utilized to assess the interaction. It is important to allow for this fact in the ultimate calculation of the standard errors of the various treatment series. The replications attributable to the treatment means from which any interaction has been calculated will be only three-quarters of that of an unconfounded experiment of the same type. In this example, for the main effects which are unconfounded, there will be 16 replications but for the first-order interactions only 6 instead of 8 and for the second-order interaction $A \times B \times C$ three instead of four replications.

The $3 \times 3 \times 3$ Confounded Experiment.—The $2 \times 2 \times 2$ experiment suffers from the obvious disadvantage that all the treatment effects in the analysis of variance are derived from a single degree of freedom, and in consequence, only large treatment differences are likely to be significant. It is, furthermore, true that, in any experiment in which a particular factor is included at only two levels, there is a very small chance of obtaining any accurate idea of the optimum level for this particular factor. For this purpose at least three levels of each factor are required, and in experiments in which great accuracy is aimed at, an even wider range of values may be included. For these reasons, the $3 \times 3 \times 3$ or 3^3 factorial experiment, involving 27 treatment combinations, must be regarded as decidedly superior to the 2^3 design. On a nonconfounded layout, a

3^3 design makes it necessary for each block to have 27 plots. Such large blocks are generally far from uniform, and they tend to obviate much of the advantage of the randomized block arrangement as a means of reducing the effects of plot heterogeneity in the statistical evaluation of the results. This disadvantage can be overcome if every block is split up into three subblocks of nine plots each, so as to confound part of the second-order interaction. There are four alternative ways of allocating the treatments to the subblocks in order to obtain the required degree of confounding. One of these selected at random is given below. This allocation was used in a tomato manurial experiment in which the fertilizers tested were sulphate of ammonia, sulphate of potash, and superphosphate, each at three rates of application, *viz.*, 0, 1, and 2 hundredweights per acre.

Subblock a	Subblock b	Subblock c
(1) $N_2 K_1 P_2$	(10) $N_1 K_2 P_0$	(19) $N_2 K_2 P_1$
(2) $N_0 K_1 P_1$	(11) $N_2 K_0 P_0$	(20) $N_0 K_0 P_1$
(3) $N_1 K_0 P_2$	(12) $N_2 K_1 P_1$	(21) $N_2 K_0 P_2$
(4) $N_1 K_2 P_1$	(13) $N_0 K_0 P_2$	(22) $N_2 K_1 P_0$
(5) $N_0 K_0 P_0$	(14) $N_0 K_1 P_0$	(23) $N_1 K_2 P_2$
(6) $N_2 K_2 P_0$	(15) $N_0 K_2 P_1$	(24) $N_0 K_2 P_0$
(7) $N_0 K_2 P_2$	(16) $N_1 K_1 P_2$	(25) $N_0 K_1 P_2$
(8) $N_2 K_0 P_1$	(17) $N_1 K_0 P_1$	(26) $N_1 K_0 P_0$
(9) $N_1 K_1 P_0$	(18) $N_2 K_2 P_2$	(27) $N_1 K_1 P_1$

TABLE 91.—YIELD OF TOMATOES IN BASKETS (10 LB.) PER $\frac{1}{50}$-ACRE PLOT

Treatment type	Subblock		Treatment type	Subblock		Treatment type	Subblock	
	Ia	IIa		Ib	IIb		Ic	IIc
1	8	6	10	10	13	19	10	8
2	8	4	11	7	3	20	7	8
3	12	6	12	9	7	21	6	5
4	10	7	13	8	4	22	7	9
5	5	6	14	10	8	23	15	11
6	5	10	15	5	7	24	10	6
7	6	4	16	14	9	25	5	7
8	9	8	17	12	5	26	9	15
9	12	10	18	7	6	27	9	5
Subblock total	75	61		82	62		78	74
						Grand total 432		

There were 54 plots in all in the experiment, giving the equivalent of two blocks (I and II) of 27 plots each to take the 27 treatment combinations. Each large block was subdivided into three subblocks *a*, *b*, and *c*, and the 27 treatments allocated to the subblocks as shown above. The arrangement of the nine treatments within any one subblock was, of course, a random one.

TABLE 92.—TREATMENT TOTALS

	N_0	N_1	N_2	K *total*		P_0	P_1	P_2	K *total*
K_0	38	59	38	*135*	K_0	45	49	41	*135*
K_1	42	59	46	*147*	K	56	42	49	*147*
K_2	38	66	46	*150*	K_2	54	47	49	*150*
N total......	*118*	*184*	*130*	*432*	P total......	*155*	*138*	*139*	*432*

	P_0	P_1	P_2	N *total*
N_0	45	39	34	*118*
N_1	69	48	67	*184*
N_2	41	51	38	*130*
P total..............	*155*	*138*	*139*	*432*

If the large blocks I and II had not been subdivided so as to confound part of the second-order interaction, the allocation of the total 53 degrees of freedom would have been as follows:

Factor	Degrees of freedom
Total......................	53
Blocks......................	1
Main effects: N..............	2 ⎫
K..............	2 ⎬ 6 for main effects
P..............	2 ⎭
Interactions:	
1st order: N × K...........	4 ⎫
N × P...........	4 ⎬ 12 for 1st-order interactions
K × P...........	4 ⎭
2d order: N × P × K.......	8
Error......................	26

On the confounded arrangement, one-quarter of the second-order interaction degrees of freedom are completely entangled with the blocks. This leaves a balance of 24 degrees of freedom for treatments. The main treatment effects and first-order interactions are not altered and can be calculated in the usual way. In most experiments of this type, the unconfounded portion of the second-order interaction—6 degrees of freedom— can be bulked in with those for error without serious loss of information. This is permissible as it is only in exceptional cases that the second-order interaction will be significant. If, for any reason, it is considered essential to evaluate this factor, it can be calculated, but as the calculation is somewhat involved, it is not proposed to attempt to describe the technique here. The appended analysis of variance can therefore be considered adequate for an accurate interpretation of results.

TABLE 93.—ANALYSIS OF VARIANCE

Factor	S.S.	Degrees of freedom	Variance
Total	422.0	53	
Blocks, *i.e.*, subblocks	41.0	5	
Treatments:			
Main effects: N	137.3	2	68.65**
K	7.0	2	3.50
P	10.1	2	5.05
Interaction: N × K	7.4	4	1.85
P × K	15.9	4	3.98
N × P	60.3	4	15.08*
Error	143.0	30	4.77

* Significant at 5 per cent point.
** Significant at 1 per cent point.

The quantity of nitrogen and the interaction of nitrogen and phosphate are the only significant factors in the analysis. A difference between the three nitrogen totals greater than 26.75 is significant, proving that the single dressing of nitrogen has given higher yields than the control or the double dressings. As the F test for the N × P interaction is positive a difference greater than $\sqrt{4.77 \times 6 \times 2} \times 2.042$ or 15.44 between any of the nine N × P totals is significant. Reference to the N × P treatment table shows that in this experiment the response to the single dressing of nitrogen is better than to the double dressing except in the presence of a light application of phosphatic manure.

The other three ways in which the treatments may be allocated to the subblocks in order to confound two of the second-order interaction degrees of freedom are shown as follows:

Subblock a	Subblock b	Subblock c
N_0 K_0 P_0	N_0 K_0 P_1	N_0 K_0 P_2
N_0 K_1 P_1	N_0 K_1 P_2	N_0 K_1 P_0
N_0 K_2 P_2	N_0 K_2 P_0	N_0 K_2 P_1
N_1 K_0 P_1	N_1 K_0 P_2	N_1 K_0 P_0
N_1 K_1 P_2	N_1 K_1 P_0	N_1 K_1 P_1
N_1 K_2 P_0	N_1 K_2 P_1	N_1 K_2 P_2
N_2 K_0 P_2	N_2 K_0 P_0	N_2 K_0 P_1
N_2 K_1 P_0	N_2 K_1 P_1	N_2 K_1 P_2
N_2 K_2 P_1	N_2 K_2 P_2	N_2 K_2 P_0

or

Subblock a	Subblock b	Subblock c
N_0 K_0 P_0	N_0 K_0 P_1	N_0 K_0 P_2
N_0 K_1 P_2	N_0 K_1 P_0	N_0 K_1 P_1
N_0 K_2 P_1	N_0 K_2 P_2	N_0 K_2 P_0
N_1 K_0 P_1	N_1 K_0 P_2	N_1 K_0 P_0
N_1 K_1 P_0	N_1 K_1 P_1	N_1 K_1 P_2
N_1 K_2 P_2	N_1 K_2 P_0	N_1 K_2 P_1
N_2 K_0 P_2	N_2 K_0 P_0	N_2 K_0 P_1
N_2 K_1 P_1	N_2 K_1 P_2	N_2 K_1 P_0
N_2 K_2 P_0	N_2 K_2 P_1	N_2 K_2 P_2

or

Subblock a	Subblock b	Subblock c
N_0 K_0 P_0	N_0 K_0 P_1	N_0 K_0 P_2
N_0 K_1 P_2	N_0 K_1 P_0	N_0 K_1 P_1
N_0 K_2 P_1	N_0 K_2 P_2	N_0 K_2 P_0
N_1 K_0 P_2	N_1 K_0 P_0	N_1 K_0 P_1
N_1 K_1 P_1	N_1 K_1 P_2	N_1 K_1 P_0
N_1 K_2 P_0	N_1 K_2 P_1	N_1 K_2 P_2
N_2 K_0 P_1	N_2 K_0 P_2	N_2 K_0 P_0
N_2 K_1 P_0	N_2 K_1 P_1	N_2 K_1 P_2
N_2 K_2 P_2	N_2 K_2 P_0	N_2 K_2 P_1

In the tomato experiment there were two complete replications of the 27 treatment combinations, and the same allocation of the treatments to the three subblocks was used for each replication. Actually, when there is more than one complete replication, it is generally considered better to select, from the four optional arrangements, a different allocation of the treatments to the subblocks for each available replication. This is really partial confounding, as a different portion of the second-order interaction will be confounded in each complete block or replication. Provided the second-order interaction variance is bulked in with the error, the analysis of variance of the data will not be altered by this partial confounding technique. It will be noted that it is only the second-order interaction that has been confounded, and in agricultural experiments in general, it is usually advisable to leave the main effects and the first-order interactions unconfounded and limit the confounding to the higher order interaction effects.

SUBDIVISION OF THE TREATMENT RESPONSES IN A 3^3 EXPERIMENT

When any factor is included in an experiment at three different levels, it is possible to split up the treatment variance to two components representing (a) the linear response due to the difference between the extreme levels and (b) the curvature, or deviation of the intermediate level from this linear response. Each component accounts for one of the available degrees of freedom. Yates gives a simple method of evaluating those components for the main effects.

If a_0, a_1, a_2 represent the individual plot yields of the factor A included at the three levels 0, 1, and 2, respectively,

$$\text{Linear response} = \frac{(\Sigma a_2 - \Sigma a_0)^2}{2n}$$

$$\text{Curvature} = \frac{(\Sigma a_2 - 2\Sigma a_1 + \Sigma a_0)^2}{6n}$$

where n represents the number of plots in any of the treatment totals evaluated in the above expressions. The linear response formula is, of course, merely another version of that already given in Chap. II for evaluating any treatment sum of squares dependent on only two totals.

Applying this technique to the main treatment effects of the tomato manurial experiment (Table 92) for the main effect K,

$$\text{Linear response} = \frac{(150 - 135)^2}{2 \times 18} = 6.25 \text{ with 1 degree of freedom}$$

$$\text{Curvature} = \frac{(150 - 2 \times 147 + 135)^2}{6 \times 18} = 0.75 \text{ with 1 degree of freedom}$$

The aggregate of the two components adds up to the total sum of squares for the main effect of potash, as given in the original analysis of variance Table 93.   The linear component accounts for the major portion of the response to potash.   With an error variance of 4.77, this linear variance is still nonsignificant. It is not impossible, however, for the linear response to be significant when the main effect as a whole is nonsignificant.   Where there is any apparent response to increasing rates of any factor, this subdivision of the treatment variance should certainly be carried out.   With the nitrogen and phosphate factors (Table 92), the higher levels have given lower yields than the lower levels, and the analysis to the two components will not be of any value. The formulas still apply, however.   For example,

$$\text{N, linear response} = \frac{(130 - 118)^2}{2 \times 18} = 4.0$$

$$\text{Curvature} = \frac{(130 - 2 \times 184 + 118)^2}{6 \times 18} = 133.3$$

$\left.\right\}$ total main effect, N = 137.3 (as originally calculated)

It is also possible to split up the first-order interaction effects between the linear response and curvature factors.   This process is not of such general utility, and as its exact significance is rather difficult to explain in simple terms, it is not proposed to elaborate it here.

A 3³ EXPERIMENT WITHOUT REPLICATION

The 3^3 factorial experiment is a particularly useful design, as it allows three factors to be tested in all combinations at a sufficient number of different levels to show up any definite treatment responses.   It is especially adapted to fertilizer experiments, as the three main types of fertilizer—N, P and K—can all be included and their interactions and optimum rates determined.   A very useful form of the 3^3 experiment is the one limited to a total of 27 plots with the second-order interaction confounded in the subblocks.   As there are 27 different treatment combinations, this means that there will be no replication of any one treatment type.   The estimate of the error variance is derived from the remaining 6 degrees of freedom of the second-order interaction after eliminating the two confounded degrees of freedom.   Such an experiment cannot be expected to give the same degree of precision as would be obtained when two or more replications of each treatment series is included. It does make it possible to lay down a fairly comprehensive type of experiment on a small acreage and at relatively low cost. Several such nonreplicated experiments at different centers would probably be much more informative than a single large-scale experiment costing about the same amount but located on only one soil type.

COMPLEX CONFOUNDED DESIGNS

The principle of confounding can be applied to many other factorial designs including 2^n, 3^n, 4^2, $3 \times 2 \times 2$, etc., treatment combinations. Many of these forms have been elaborated by Yates.* With high degrees of confounding, the statistical analysis tends to become somewhat involved, especially when the factors are included at varying levels as in a $3 \times 2 \times 2$ experiment. The principle has also been adapted to the Latin square, though its application in this direction is of necessity very much more limited. A very useful form of this in a 3^3 factorial experiment is a 9×9 Latin square in which the second-order interaction is confounded with both the rows and the columns of the square.

TABLE 94.—A 9×9 QUASI-LATIN SQUARE FOR A 3^3 FACTORIAL EXPERIMENT WITH THE 2D-ORDER INTERACTION CONFOUNDED IN THE ROWS AND COLUMNS

$A_0 B_0 C_0$	$A_1 B_0 C_1$	$A_2 B_0 C_2$	$A_0 B_1 C_1$	$A_1 B_1 C_2$	$A_2 B_1 C_0$	$A_0 B_2 C_2$	$A_1 B_2 C_0$	$A_2 B_2 C_1$
1 0 1	2 0 2	0 0 0	1 1 2	2 1 0	0 1 1	2 2 1	0 2 2	1 2 0
2 0 2	0 0 0	1 0 1	2 1 0	0 1 1	1 1 2	1 2 0	2 2 1	0 2 2
0 1 2	2 1 1	1 1 0	2 2 2	1 2 1	0 2 0	2 0 0	0 0 1	1 0 2
1 1 0	0 1 2	2 1 1	0 2 0	2 2 2	1 2 1	0 0 1	1 0 2	2 0 0
2 1 1	1 1 0	0 1 2	1 2 1	0 2 0	2 2 2	1 0 2	2 0 0	0 0 1
0 2 1	2 2 0	1 2 2	0 0 2	2 0 1	1 0 0	0 1 0	2 1 2	1 1 1
1 2 2	0 2 1	2 2 0	1 0 0	0 0 2	2 0 1	2 1 2	1 1 1	0 1 0
2 2 0	1 2 2	0 2 1	2 0 1	1 0 0	0 0 2	1 1 1	0 1 0	2 1 2

* The Design and Analysis of Factorial Experiments, *Imp. Bur. Soil Sci. Tech. Comm.* 35.

A square of this type is termed a *quasi-Latin square*. Any of the alternative arrangements already enumerated for the confounding of the $A \times B \times C$ interaction in a 3^3 design may be used to construct such a square. Yates gives the following design. The three factors concerned are A, B, and C, each at the three levels 0, 1, and 2. It will be assumed that the numbers tabulated in each plot represent, from left to right, the levels of the three factors in the order A, B, C, as entered in full in the first row. Thus, the treatment in the bottom right-hand corner plot is $A_2B_1C_2$.

Provided a new randomization of the complete rows and the complete columns is effected on each occasion, this design may be used as a standard form for fixing the layout of a field experiment of this type. If one assumes that the second-order interaction effects may safely be bulked in with the error sum of squares, the analysis of variance is perfectly simple, being of the type:

	Degrees of freedom
Total	80
Rows	8
Columns	8
Treatments: Main effects	6
1st-order interactions	12
Error	46

Confounding in Split-plot Design.—Another useful form, involving confounding in a Latin-square layout, is the one applicable to the split-plot experiment in which there are six whole-plot treatments, A, B, C, D, E, and F in a 6×6 Latin square, combined with subplot treatments of the $2 \times 2 \times 2$ factorial type. There will then be eight subplot treatment combinations, which will be most easily comprehended by using symbols appropriate to a 2^3 fertilizer experiment with each of the three main fertilizers at two rates. On this assumption, the subplot treatments would be of the type

(I) n, p, k, npk
(II) 0, np, nk, pk

By splitting these eight combinations into two groups of four as shown above in the lines I and II, the second-order interaction

N × P × K is confounded with the groups. This fact can be utilized in the split-plot experiment by subdividing each whole plot to four subplots and allocating one or other group of subplot treatments to each whole plot in accordance with the appended design.

A^{I}	F^{II}	D^{II}	E^{II}	B^{I}	C^{I}
D^{I}	C^{II}	A^{II}	B^{II}	E^{I}	F^{I}
B^{I}	D^{II}	E^{II}	F^{II}	C^{I}	A^{I}
C^{I}	E^{II}	F^{II}	D^{II}	A^{I}	B^{I}
F^{I}	B^{II}	C^{II}	A^{II}	D^{I}	E^{I}
E^{I}	A^{II}	B^{II}	C^{II}	F^{I}	D^{I}

Each square on the diagram represents a whole plot, and the letters specify the whole-plot treatment. The prefixes I or II attached to the letters indicate the particular group of subplot treatments which should be randomized among the four subplot units to which this whole plot is split up. With this design the second-order subplot treatment interaction N × P × K is confounded with the columns, and the third-order interaction between the whole-plot and subplot treatments is confounded with the rows. The statistical analysis, ignoring the two confounded treatment effects, will be of the type tabulated on page 240.

The general principle of confounding certain subplot treatment effects in a split-plot experiment is worth noting, as it makes it possible to adopt a relatively small whole-plot unit, lessens the size of the whole-plot blocks, and increases the number of whole-plot treatment replications. It therefore overcomes some of the disadvantages associated with the split-plot design.

The practice of confounding applied to field experiments has been discussed at some length, as it appears to be the direction from which the greatest immediate improvement in experimental design may be expected. The advantage of confounding lies in the practicability of planning an efficient experiment involving several treatment series in all combinations on a relatively small

	Degrees of freedom
Whole plots	35
Rows	*5*
Columns	*5*
Whole-plot treatments (*W*)	*5*
Error (*a*)	*20*
Total subplots	143
Subplot treatments:	
Main effects	3
First-order interactions N × P, N × K, P × K	3
Interactions:	
Whole-plot treatment (*W*) × subplot treatment	
W × main effects	15
W × first-order interactions	15
Error (*b*)	72

area. The introduction of the subblock arrangement associated with the confounded experiment ensures better control of the soil heterogeneity factor than would otherwise be possible with the large blocks necessary to a nonconfounded experiment of the same general type. On the other hand, confounding is only practicable in complex experiments of a rather specialized character, and it is a system that can be wholeheartedly recommended only when the man in charge is sure of his technique both in the field and also in the statistical office, where the final evaluation of the data will be effected.

VALEDICTORY REMARKS

It is considered that further discussion of more complex experimental designs would be definitely out-of-place in an elementary textbook on applied statistics. It is hoped that sufficient examples have been given to demonstrate that for established forms of experiment the statistical calculations may be reduced to a simple routine which leaves no excuse for any ambiguity in the interpretation of the results.

In 1849, in the preface to his "Experimental Agriculture," J. F. W. Johnston wrote:

It is only by means of conjoined experiments in the field, the feeding house and the laboratory—*all made with equal care, conscientiousness and precision*—that scientific agriculture can hereafter be with certainty advanced. If we have been long in getting upon the right road, we ought to advance the more heartily now we have found it.

The following quotation from the title page of the earlier numbers of the *Journal of the Royal Agricultural Society of England* is also very apt:

These experiments, it is true are not easy; still they are in the power of every thinking husbandman. He who accomplishes but one, of however limited application, and takes care to report it faithfully, advances the subject and consequently, the practice of agriculture, and acquires thereby a right to the gratitude of his fellows, and of those who come after. . . . The first care of all societies formed for the improvement of our science should be to prepare the forms of such experiments, and to distribute the execution of these among their members.

This last sentence effectively summarizes the author's aim in preparing this elementary exposition of statistical methods, which it is hoped may ultimately prove of some value in the distribution and correct application of certain of the existing forms of experiment.

SELECTED BIBLIOGRAPHY

A. General Works on Statistical Theory and Practice

1. Bibliography of Statistical Methods and Their Application to Agronomy, by K. K. Guha Roy, and P. C. Māhalanobis. *Imp. Council Agr. Res. India, Misc. Bull.* 9, 1936. 120 pp.
2. Experimental Error, The Theory of, by F. L. Engledow. *J. Min. of Agr. London*, 32: 326–333, 1926.
3. Mathematics and Agronomy, by "Student." *J. Amer. Soc. Agron.*, 18: 703–719, 1926.
4. "Outline of Biometric Analysis, An," by Alan E. Treloar. Burgess Pub. Co., Minneapolis, 1935.
5. Paired Experiments, "Student's" Method for Interpreting, by H. H. Love and A. M. Brunson. *J. Amer. Soc. Agron.*, 16: 60–68, 1924.
6. Probable Error of a Mean, The, by "Student." *Biometrika*, 6: 1–26, 1908.
7. Sampling, Estimation of Efficiency of, by F. Yates and I. Zacopanay. *J. Agr. Sci.*, 25: 545–577, 1935.
8. Sampling Technique, Studies in, by A. R. Clapham. *J. Agr. Sci.*, 21: 376–390, 1931.
9. "Statistical Methods," by G. W. Snedecor. Collegiate Press, Iowa, 1937.
10. "Statistical Methods for Research Workers," by R. A. Fisher. Oliver & Boyd, Edinburgh, 5th ed., 1934. 319 pp.
11. "Statistical Methods to Agricultural Research, Application of," by H. H. Love. Commercial Press, Shanghai, 1936.
12. "Statistics, An Introduction to the Theory of," by G. U. Yule. Griffin and Co., Ltd., London, 9th ed., 1929. 416 pp.
13. "Statistics for use in Plant Breeding and Agricultural Problems, A Handbook of," by F. J. F. Shaw. Government of India, Delhi, 1936. 182 pp.
14. "Statistics, The Methods of," by L. H. C. Tippett. Williams and Norgate, London, 1930. 222 pp.
15. z Test When Applied to Non-normal Data, The Validity of Fisher's, by T. Eden and F. Yates. *J. Agr. Sci.*, 23: 6–17, 1933.

B. Analysis of Variance

16. "Bibliography of Statistical Methods, Chiefly on the Application of the Analysis of Variance," by Ch. Zinzadze. Issued by Rothamsted Experiment Station, 1933. 27 pp.
17. Experimental Error, by E. J. Maskell. *Trop. Agr.*, 5: 306–309; 6: 5–11, 45–48, 97–99, 1928.

18. Inter-relation of Factors Controlling the Production of Cotton, by F. G. Gregory, F. Crowther, and A. D. Lambert. *J. Agr. Sci.*, 22: 617–638, 1932.
19. Orthogonality in Confounding and Replicated Experiments, The Principles of, by F. Yates. *J. Agr. Sci.*, 23: 108–145, 1933.
20. Residual Variance in Field Experiments, A Note on, by W. H. Beckett. *Trop. Agr.*, 9: 7–10, 1932.
21. Variance Analyses to Experiments in Field Chemistry, The Application of, by C. H. Goulden. *Cereal Chem.*, 9: 239–260, 1932.

C. Correlation, Regression, and Covariance

22. Correlation and Regression in Statistical Analysis, A Note on the Value of, by D. D. Paterson. *Trop. Agr.*, 11: 160–169, 220–229, 1934.
23. Covariance Applicable to Previous Crop Records, The Method of, by M. Vaidyanathan. *Indian J. Agr. Sci.*, 4: 327–342, 1934.
24. Covariance in Analysing Field Experimental Data, The Value of, by F. H. Garner, J. Grantham, and H. G. Sanders. *J. Agr. Sci.*, 24: 250–259, 1934.
25. Covariance in Dairy Cow Nutrition Experiments, Value of, by M. S. Bartlett. *J. Agr. Sci.*, 25: 238–244, 1935.
26. "Genetics in Relation to Agriculture," by E. B. Babcock and R. E. Clausen. McGraw-Hill Book Company, Inc., New York, 1927. 673 pp.
27. Pig-feeding Experiment, A Complex, by F. Yates. *J. Agr. Sci.*, 24: 511–531, 1934.
28. Study in Sampling Technique with Wheat, A, by R. J. Kalamkar. *J. Agr. Sci.*, 22: 783–796, 1932.
29. Uniformity Trials for Subsequent Experimentation. A Note on the value of, by H. G. Sanders. *J. Agr. Sci.*, 20: 63–73, 1930.

D. Field Experiments

30. Analysis of Replicated Experiments When the Field Results Are Incomplete, by F. Yates. *Emp. J. Exp. Agr.*, 1: 129–142, 1933.
31. "Design of Field Experiments, The," by R. A. Fisher. Oliver & Boyd, Edinburgh, 1935. 252 pp.
32. Experimental Determination of Value of Top Dressings with Cereals, The, by T. Eden and R. A. Fisher. *J. Agr. Sci.*, 17: 548–562, 1927.
33. Experimental Errors of Field Experiments with Tea, The, by T. Eden. *Tea Res. Inst., Ceylon, Bull.* 6, 1931.
34. Experimentation and Applied Statistics for the Practical Agriculturist, by D. D. Paterson. *Trop. Agr.*, 10: 267–276, 303–317, 346–351, 1933.
35. Factorial Experiments, The Design and Analysis of, by F. Yates. *Imp. Bur. Soil Sci., Tech. Comm.* 35.
36. Field Experimentation, Modern Methods of, by C. H. Goulden. *Sci. Agr. (Canada)*, 11: 681–701, 1931.
37. "Field Experiments": How They Are Made and What They Are! by Sir J. Russell. *J. Min. Agr., London*, 32: 989–1001, 1926.
38. Field Experiments in Horticulture, by T. N. Hoblyn. *Imp. Bur. Fruit Prod., Tech. Comm.* 2 (1931), pp. 50.

39. Field Experiments, The Arrangement of, by R. A. Fisher. *J. Min. Agr., London*, 33: 503–513, 1926.
40. Field Experiments, The Conduct of, by R. O. Iliffe and B. Viswa Nath. *Dept. Agr. Madras, Bull.* 89, 1928.
41. Field Trials and the Statistical Reduction of Results, The Arrangement of, by R. A. Fisher and J. Wishart. *Imp. Bur. Soil Sci. Tech. Comm.* 10, 1930.
42. Latin Squares for Use in Field Experiments, The Formation of, by F. Yates. *Emp. J. Exp. Agr.*, 1: 235–244, 1933.
43. Manurial Experiments with Sugar Cane, by P. E. Turner and J. A. Potter. *Trop. Agr.*, 9: 44–53, 1932.
44. Missing Plot in Field Experimental Work, A Method of Estimating the Yield of a, by F. E. Allan and J. Wishart. *J. Agr. Sci.*, 20: 399–406, 1930.
45. Modern Field Experiments, by T. Eden. *Trop. Agrst. (Ceylon)*, 71: 67–76, 1928.
46. Principles and Practice of Yield Trials, The, by F. L. Engledow and G. U. Yule. *Emp. Cotton Growing Rev.*, 3: 112–146, 1926.
47. "Principles and Practice of Yield Trials," by J. Wishart and H. G. Sanders. Published by Empire Cotton Growing Corp., 1935. 100 pp.
48. Sampling Technique with Wheat, A Study in, by R. J. Kalamkar. *J. Agr. Sci.*, 22: 783–796, 1932.
49. Shape of Plots in Field Experimentation, The Importance of the, by B. G. Christidis. *J. Agr. Sci.*, 21: 14–37, 1931.
50. Statistical Methods for Field Experiments, *Agr. Dept. S. Africa, Sci. Bull.* 147, 1935.
51. Systematic Plot Arrangement on the Estimate of Error in Field Experiments, The Influence of, by O. Tedin. *J. Agr. Sci.*, 21: 191–208, 1931.
52. "Technique of Field Experiments. The," Report of Rothamsted Conference 13, 1931. 54 pp.
53. Technique of Modern Field Experiments, by E. M. Crowther. *J. Roy. Agr. Soc. England*, 97: 54–80.
54. Trials of New Varieties of Cereals, by E. S. Beaven. *J. Min. Agr., London*, 29: 337–347, 436–444, 1922.
55. Uniformity Trials in Field Experimentation with Rubber, The Value of, by R. K. S. Murray. *J. Agr. Sci.*, 24: 177–184, 1934.
56. Uniformity Trials on Cocoa, by E. E. Cheesman and F. J. Pound. *Trop. Agr.*, 9: 277–288, 1932.
57. Uniformity Trials Useful, Are, by H. H. Love. *J. Amer. Soc. Agron.*, 28: 234–245, 1936.
58. Yield Trials, by "Student," Baillière's Encyclopedia of Scientific Agriculture, edited by H. Hunter. Vol. II, pp. 1342–1361, 1931.

E. Mathematical and Statistical Tables

59. Auxiliary Tables for Fisher's z Test in the Analysis of Variance, by P. C. Mahalanobis. *Indian J. Agr. Sci.*, 2: 679–695, 1932.

60. "Barlow's Tables of Squares, Cubes, Square Roots, Cube Roots and Reciprocals of all Integral Numbers up to 10,000," edited by L. J. Comrie. E. & F. N. Spon, Ltd., London, 3d ed., 1930. 208 pp.

61. Mathematical Tables, Four-figure, by J. T. Bottomley. Macmillan and Company, Ltd., London, 1928.

62. Random Sampling Numbers, by L. H. C. Tippett, edited by K. Pearson. Tracts for Computors No. XV, University of London, 1927. 50 pp.

63. "Statistical Tables for Biological, Medical, and Agricultural Research," by R. A. Fisher and F. Yates. Edinburgh, 1937.

64. "Tables for Statisticians and Biometricians," by K. Pearson. Cambridge University Press, Parts I and II, 1932.

65. "Tables of $\sqrt{1 - r^2}$ and $1 - r^2$," by J. R. Miner. Johns Hopkins Press, Baltimore, 1922.

APPENDIX

STATISTICAL TABLES

TABLE I.—TABLE OF x^*

The deviation in the normal distribution in terms of the standard deviation

P†	0.01	0.02	0.03	0.04	0.05	0.06	0.07	0.08	0.09	0.10
0.00	2.575829	2.326348	2.170090	2.053749	1.959964	1.880794	1.811911	1.750686	1.695398	1.644854
0.10	1.598193	1.554774	1.514102	1.475791	1.439521	1.405072	1.372204	1.340755	1.310579	1.281552
0.20	1.253565	1.226528	1.200359	1.174987	1.150349	1.126391	1.103063	1.080319	1.058122	1.036433
0.30	1.015222	0.994458	0.974114	0.954165	0.934589	0.915365	0.896473	0.877896	0.859617	0.841621
0.40	0.823894	0.806421	0.789192	0.772193	0.755415	0.738847	0.722479	0.706303	0.690309	0.674490
0.50	0.658838	0.643345	0.628006	0.612813	0.597760	0.582841	0.568051	0.553385	0.538836	0.524401
0.60	0.510073	0.495850	0.481727	0.467699	0.453762	0.439913	0.426148	0.412463	0.398855	0.385320
0.70	0.371856	0.358459	0.345125	0.331853	0.318639	0.305481	0.292375	0.279319	0.266311	0.253347
0.80	0.240426	0.227545	0.214702	0.201893	0.189118	0.176374	0.163658	0.150969	0.138304	0.125661
0.90	0.113039	0.100434	0.087845	0.075270	0.062707	0.050154	0.037608	0.025069	0.012533	0

* Reproduced by kind permission of Professor R. A. Fisher and of his publishers, Messrs. Oliver & Boyd, Edinburgh.

† The value of P for each entry is obtained by adding the column value to that of the row. For example, for $x = 1.200359$, P = 0.23.

TABLE II.—TABLE OF t*

n	$P = 0.9$	0.8	0.7	0.6	0.5	0.4	0.3	0.2	0.1	0.05	0.02	0.01
1	0.158	0.325	0.510	0.727	1.000	1.376	1.963	3.078	6.314	12.706	31.821	63.657
2	0.142	0.289	0.445	0.617	0.816	1.061	1.386	1.886	2.920	4.303	6.965	9.925
3	0.137	0.277	0.424	0.584	0.765	0.978	1.250	1.638	2.353	3.182	4.541	5.841
4	0.134	0.271	0.414	0.569	0.741	0.941	1.190	1.533	2.132	2.776	3.747	4.604
5	0.132	0.267	0.408	0.559	0.727	0.920	1.156	1.476	2.015	2.571	3.365	4.032
6	0.131	0.265	0.404	0.553	0.718	0.906	1.134	1.440	1.943	2.447	3.143	3.707
7	0.130	0.263	0.402	0.549	0.711	0.896	1.119	1.415	1.895	2.365	2.998	3.499
8	0.130	0.262	0.399	0.546	0.706	0.889	1.108	1.397	1.860	2.306	2.896	3.355
9	0.129	0.261	0.398	0.543	0.703	0.883	1.100	1.383	1.833	2.262	2.821	3.250
10	0.129	0.260	0.397	0.542	0.700	0.879	1.093	1.372	1.812	2.228	2.764	3.169
11	0.129	0.260	0.396	0.540	0.697	0.876	1.088	1.363	1.796	2.201	2.718	3.106
12	0.128	0.259	0.395	0.539	0.695	0.873	1.083	1.356	1.782	2.179	2.681	3.055
13	0.128	0.259	0.394	0.538	0.694	0.870	1.079	1.350	1.771	2.160	2.650	3.012
14	0.128	0.258	0.393	0.537	0.692	0.868	1.076	1.345	1.761	2.145	2.624	2.977
15	0.128	0.258	0.393	0.536	0.691	0.866	1.074	1.341	1.753	2.131	2.602	2.947
16	0.128	0.258	0.392	0.535	0.690	0.865	1.071	1.337	1.746	2.120	2.583	2.921
17	0.128	0.257	0.392	0.534	0.689	0.863	1.069	1.333	1.740	2.110	2.567	2.898
18	0.127	0.257	0.392	0.534	0.688	0.862	1.067	1.330	1.734	2.101	2.552	2.878
19	0.127	0.257	0.391	0.533	0.688	0.861	1.066	1.328	1.729	2.093	2.539	2.861
20	0.127	0.257	0.391	0.533	0.687	0.860	1.064	1.325	1.725	2.086	2.528	2.845
21	0.127	0.257	0.391	0.532	0.686	0.859	1.063	1.323	1.721	2.080	2.518	2.831
22	0.127	0.256	0.390	0.532	0.686	0.858	1.061	1.321	1.717	2.074	2.508	2.819
23	0.127	0.256	0.390	0.532	0.685	0.858	1.060	1.319	1.714	2.069	2.500	2.807
24	0.127	0.256	0.390	0.531	0.685	0.857	1.059	1.318	1.711	2.064	2.492	2.797
25	0.127	0.256	0.390	0.531	0.684	0.856	1.058	1.316	1.708	2.060	2.485	2.787
26	0.127	0.256	0.390	0.531	0.684	0.856	1.058	1.315	1.706	2.056	2.479	2.779
27	0.127	0.256	0.389	0.531	0.684	0.855	1.057	1.314	1.703	2.052	2.473	2.771
28	0.127	0.256	0.389	0.530	0.683	0.855	1.056	1.313	1.701	2.048	2.467	2.763
29	0.127	0.256	0.389	0.530	0.683	0.854	1.055	1.311	1.699	2.045	2.462	2.756
30	0.127	0.256	0.389	0.530	0.683	0.854	1.055	1.310	1.697	2.042	2.457	2.750
∞	0.12566	0.25335	0.38532	0.52440	0.67449	0.84162	1.03643	1.28155	1.64485	1.95996	2.32634	2.57582

* Reproduced by kind permission of Professor R. A. Fisher and of his publishers, Messrs. Oliver & Boyd, Edinburgh.

Table III.—5 Per Cent Points of the Distribution of z*

Values of n_2	Values of n_1: 1	2	3	4	5	6	8	12	24	α
1	2.5421	2.6479	2.6870	2.7071	2.7194	2.7276	2.7380	2.7484	2.7588	2.7693
1′	1.4592	1.4722	1.4765	1.4787	1.4800	1.4808	1.4819	1.4830	1.4840	1.4851
3	1.1577	1.1284	1.1137	1.1051	1.0994	1.0953	1.0899	1.0842	1.0781	1.0716
4	1.0212	0.9690	0.9429	0.9272	0.9168	0.9093	0.8993	0.8885	0.8767	0.8639
5	0.9441	0.8777	0.8441	0.8236	0.8097	0.7997	0.7862	0.7714	0.7550	0.7368
6	0.8948	0.8188	0.7798	0.7558	0.7394	0.7274	0.7112	0.6931	0.6729	0.6499
7	0.8606	0.7777	0.7347	0.7080	0.6896	0.6761	0.6576	0.6369	0.6134	0.5862
8	0.8355	0.7475	0.7014	0.6725	0.6525	0.6378	0.6175	0.5945	0.5682	0.5371
9	0.8163	0.7242	0.6757	0.6450	0.6238	0.6080	0.5862	0.5613	0.5324	0.4979
10	0.8012	0.7058	0.6553	0.6232	0.6009	0.5843	0.5611	0.5346	0.5035	0.4657
11	0.7889	0.6909	0.6387	0.6055	0.5822	0.5648	0.5406	0.5126	0.4795	0.4387
12	0.7788	0.6786	0.6250	0.5907	0.5666	0.5487	0.5234	0.4941	0.4592	0.4156
13	0.7703	0.6682	0.6134	0.5783	0.5535	0.5350	0.5089	0.4785	0.4419	0.3957
14	0.7630	0.6594	0.6036	0.5677	0.5423	0.5233	0.4964	0.4649	0.4269	0.3782
15	0.7568	0.6518	0.5950	0.5585	0.5326	0.5131	0.4855	0.4532	0.4138	0.3628
16	0.7514	0.6451	0.5876	0.5505	0.5241	0.5042	0.4760	0.4428	0.4022	0.3490
17	0.7466	0.6393	0.5811	0.5434	0.5166	0.4964	0.4676	0.4337	0.3919	0.3366
18	0.7424	0.6341	0.5753	0.5371	0.5099	0.4894	0.4602	0.4255	0.3827	0.3253
19	0.7386	0.6295	0.5701	0.5315	0.5040	0.4832	0.4535	0.4182	0.3743	0.3151
20	0.7352	0.6254	0.5654	0.5265	0.4986	0.4776	0.4474	0.4116	0.3668	0.3057
21	0.7322	0.6216	0.5612	0.5219	0.4938	0.4725	0.4420	0.4055	0.3599	0.2971
22	0.7294	0.6182	0.5574	0.5178	0.4894	0.4679	0.4370	0.4001	0.3536	0.2892
23	0.7269	0.6151	0.5540	0.5140	0.4854	0.4636	0.4325	0.3950	0.3478	0.2818
24	0.7246	0.6123	0.5508	0.5106	0.4817	0.4598	0.4283	0.3904	0.3425	0.2749
25	0.7225	0.6097	0.5478	0.5074	0.4783	0.4562	0.4244	0.3862	0.3376	0.2685
26	0.7205	0.6073	0.5451	0.5045	0.4752	0.4529	0.4209	0.3823	0.3330	0.2625
27	0.7187	0.6051	0.5427	0.5017	0.4723	0.4499	0.4176	0.3786	0.3287	0.2569
28	0.7171	0.6030	0.5403	0.4992	0.4696	0.4471	0.4146	0.3752	0.3248	0.2516
29	0.7155	0.6011	0.5382	0.4969	0.4671	0.4444	0.4117	0.3720	0.3211	0.2466
30	0.7141	0.5994	0.5362	0.4947	0.4648	0.4420	0.4090	0.3691	0.3176	0.2419
60	0.6933	0.5738	0.5073	0.4632	0.4311	0.4064	0.3702	0.3255	0.2654	0.1644
∞	0.6729	0.5486	0.4787	0.4319	0.3974	0.3706	0.3309	0.2804	0.2085	0.

* Reproduced by kind permission of Professor R. A. Fisher and of his publishers, Messrs. Oliver & Boyd, Edinburgh.

TABLE IV.—TABLE OF χ^2*

n	$P = 0.99$	0.98	0.95	0.90	0.80	0.70	0.50	0.30	0.20	0.10	0.05	0.02	0.01
1	0.000157	0.000628	0.00393	0.0158	0.0642	0.148	0.455	1.074	1.642	2.706	3.841	5.412	6.635
2	0.0201	0.0404	0.103	0.211	0.446	0.713	1.386	2.408	3.219	4.605	5.991	7.824	9.210
3	0.115	0.185	0.352	0.584	1.005	1.424	2.366	3.665	4.642	6.251	7.815	9.837	11.341
4	0.297	0.429	0.711	1.064	1.649	2.195	3.357	4.878	5.989	7.779	9.488	11.668	13.277
5	0.554	0.752	1.145	1.610	2.343	3.000	4.351	6.064	7.289	9.236	11.070	13.388	15.086
6	0.872	1.134	1.635	2.204	3.070	3.828	5.348	7.231	8.558	10.645	12.592	15.033	16.812
7	1.239	1.564	2.167	2.833	3.822	4.671	6.346	8.383	9.803	12.017	14.067	16.622	18.475
8	1.646	2.032	2.733	3.490	4.594	5.527	7.344	9.524	11.030	13.362	15.507	18.168	20.090
9	2.088	2.532	3.325	4.168	5.380	6.393	8.343	10.656	12.242	14.684	16.919	19.679	21.666
10	2.558	3.059	3.940	4.865	6.179	7.267	9.342	11.781	13.442	15.987	18.307	21.161	23.209
11	3.053	3.609	4.575	5.578	6.989	8.148	10.341	12.899	14.631	17.275	19.675	22.618	24.725
12	3.571	4.178	5.226	6.304	7.807	9.034	11.340	14.011	15.812	18.549	21.026	24.054	26.217
13	4.107	4.765	5.892	7.042	8.634	9.926	12.340	15.119	16.985	19.812	22.362	25.472	27.688
14	4.660	5.368	6.571	7.790	9.467	10.821	13.339	16.222	18.151	21.064	23.685	26.873	29.141
15	5.229	5.985	7.261	8.547	10.307	11.721	14.339	17.322	19.311	22.307	24.996	28.259	30.578
16	5.812	6.614	7.962	9.312	11.152	12.624	15.338	18.418	20.465	23.542	26.296	29.633	32.000
17	6.408	7.255	8.672	10.085	12.002	13.531	16.338	19.511	21.615	24.769	27.587	30.995	33.409
18	7.015	7.906	9.390	10.865	12.857	14.440	17.338	20.601	22.760	25.989	28.869	32.346	34.805
19	7.633	8.567	10.117	11.651	13.716	15.352	18.338	21.689	23.900	27.204	30.144	33.687	36.191
20	8.260	9.237	10.851	12.443	14.578	16.266	19.337	22.775	25.038	28.412	31.410	35.020	37.566
21	8.897	9.915	11.591	13.240	15.445	17.182	20.337	23.858	26.171	29.615	32.671	36.343	38.932
22	9.542	10.600	12.338	14.041	16.314	18.101	21.337	24.939	27.301	30.813	33.924	37.659	40.289
23	10.196	11.293	13.091	14.848	17.187	19.021	22.337	26.018	28.429	32.007	35.172	38.968	41.638
24	10.856	11.992	13.848	15.659	18.062	19.943	23.337	27.096	29.553	33.196	36.415	40.270	42.980
25	11.524	12.697	14.611	16.473	18.940	20.867	24.337	28.172	30.675	34.382	37.652	41.566	44.314
26	12.198	13.409	15.379	17.292	19.820	21.792	25.336	29.246	31.795	35.563	38.885	42.856	45.642
27	12.879	14.125	16.151	18.114	20.703	22.719	26.336	30.319	32.912	36.741	40.113	44.140	46.963
28	13.565	14.847	16.928	18.939	21.588	23.647	27.336	31.391	34.027	37.916	41.337	45.419	48.278
29	14.256	15.574	17.708	19.768	22.475	24.577	28.336	32.461	35.139	39.087	42.557	46.693	49.588
30	14.953	16.306	18.493	20.599	23.364	25.508	29.336	33.530	36.250	40.256	43.773	47.962	50.892

For larger values of n, the expression $\sqrt{2\chi^2} - \sqrt{2n - 1}$ may be used as a normal deviate with unit variance.

* Reproduced by kind permission of Professor R. A. Fisher and of his publishers, Messrs. Oliver & Boyd, Edinburgh.

Examples of Napierian Logarithms (Table V, pages 252–253)

$$\log_e 3.542 = 1.2647$$
$$\log_e 35.42 = 1.2647 + \log_e 10$$
$$= 1.2647 + 2.3026$$
$$= 3.5673$$
$$\log_e 0.03542 = 1.2647 - \log_e 10^2$$
$$= 1.2647 - 4.6052$$
$$= \overline{4}.6595$$

TABLE V.—NAPIERIAN LOGARITHMS*

	0	1	2	3	4	5	6	7	8	9	Mean differences								
											1	2	3	4	5	6	7	8	9
1.0	0.0000	0099	0198	0296	0392	0488	0583	0677	0770	0862	10	19	29	38	48	57	67	76	86
1.1	.0953	1044	1133	1222	1310	1398	1484	1570	1655	1740	9	17	26	35	44	52	61	70	78
1.2	.1823	1906	1989	2070	2151	2231	2311	2390	2469	2546	8	16	24	32	40	48	56	64	72
1.3	.2624	2700	2776	2852	2927	3001	3075	3148	3221	3293	7	15	22	30	37	44	52	59	67
1.4	.3365	3436	3507	3577	3646	3716	3784	3853	3920	3988	7	14	21	28	35	41	48	55	62
1.5	.4055	4121	4187	4253	4318	4383	4447	4511	4574	4637	6	13	19	26	32	39	45	52	58
1.6	.4700	4762	4824	4886	4947	5008	5068	5128	5188	5247	6	12	18	24	30	36	42	48	55
1.7	.5306	5365	5423	5481	5539	5596	5653	5710	5766	5822	6	11	17	24	29	34	40	46	51
1.8	.5878	5933	5988	6043	6098	6152	6206	6259	6313	6366	5	11	16	22	27	32	38	43	49
1.9	.6419	6471	6523	6575	6627	6678	6729	6780	6831	6881	5	10	15	20	26	31	36	41	46
2.0	.6931	6981	7031	7080	7129	7178	7227	7275	7324	7372	5	10	15	20	24	29	34	39	44
2.1	.7419	7467	7514	7561	7608	7655	7701	7747	7793	7839	5	9	14	19	23	28	33	37	42
2.2	.7885	7930	7975	8020	8065	8109	8154	8198	8242	8286	4	9	13	18	22	27	31	36	40
2.3	.8329	8372	8416	8459	8502	8544	8587	8629	8671	8713	4	9	13	17	21	26	30	34	38
2.4	.8755	8796	8838	8879	8920	8961	9002	9042	9083	9123	4	8	12	16	20	24	29	33	37
2.5	.9163	9203	9243	9282	9322	9361	9400	9439	9478	9517	4	8	12	16	20	24	27	31	35
2.6	.9555	9594	9632	9670	9708	9746	9783	9821	9858	9895	4	8	11	15	19	23	26	30	34
2.7	.9933	9969	1.0006	0043	0080	0116	0152	0188	0225	0260	4	7	11	15	18	22	25	29	33
2.8	1.0296	0332	0367	0403	0438	0473	0508	0543	0578	0613	4	7	11	14	18	21	25	28	32
2.9	1.0647	0682	0716	0750	0784	0818	0852	0886	0919	0953	3	7	10	14	17	20	24	27	31
3.0	1.0986	1019	1053	1086	1119	1151	1184	1217	1249	1282	3	7	10	13	16	20	23	26	30
3.1	1.1314	1346	1378	1410	1442	1474	1506	1537	1569	1600	3	6	10	13	16	19	22	25	29
3.2	1.1632	1663	1694	1725	1756	1787	1817	1848	1878	1909	3	6	9	12	15	18	22	25	28
3.3	1.1939	1969	1.2000	2030	2060	2090	2119	2149	2179	2208	3	6	9	12	15	18	21	24	27
3.4	1.2238	2267	2296	2326	2355	2384	2413	2442	2470	2499	3	6	9	12	15	17	20	23	26
3.5	1.2528	2556	2585	2613	2641	2669	2698	2726	2754	2782	3	6	8	11	14	17	20	23	25
3.6	1.2809	2837	2865	2892	2920	2947	2975	3002	3029	3056	3	5	8	11	14	16	19	22	25
3.7	1.3083	3110	3137	3164	3191	3218	3244	3271	3297	3324	3	5	8	11	13	16	19	21	24
3.8	1.3350	3376	3403	3429	3455	3481	3507	3533	3558	3584	3	5	8	10	13	16	18	21	23
3.9	1.3610	3635	3661	3686	3712	3737	3762	3788	3813	3838	3	5	8	10	13	15	18	20	23
4.0	1.3863	3888	3913	3938	3962	3987	4012	4036	4061	4085	2	5	7	10	12	15	17	20	22
4.1	1.4110	4134	4159	4183	4207	4231	4255	4279	4303	4327	2	5	7	10	12	14	17	19	22
4.2	1.4351	4375	4398	4422	4446	4469	4493	4516	4540	4563	2	5	7	9	12	14	16	19	21
4.3	1.4586	4609	4633	4656	4679	4702	4725	4748	4770	4793	2	5	7	9	12	14	16	18	21
4.4	1.4816	4839	4861	4884	4907	4929	4951	4974	4996	5019	2	5	7	9	11	14	16	18	20
4.5	1.5041	5063	5085	5107	5129	5151	5173	5195	5217	5239	2	4	7	9	11	13	15	18	20
4.6	1.5261	5282	5304	5326	5347	5369	5390	5412	5433	5454	2	4	6	9	11	13	15	17	19
4.7	1.5476	5497	5518	5539	5560	5581	5602	5623	5644	5665	2	4	6	8	11	13	15	17	19
4.8	1.5686	5707	5728	5748	5769	5790	5810	5831	5851	5872	2	4	6	8	10	12	14	16	19
4.9	1.5892	5913	5933	5953	5974	5994	6014	6034	6054	6074	2	4	6	8	10	12	14	16	18
5.0	1.6094	6114	6134	6154	6174	6194	6214	6233	6253	6273	2	4	6	8	10	12	14	16	18
5.1	1.6292	6312	6332	6351	6371	6390	6409	6429	6448	6467	2	4	6	8	10	12	14	16	18
5.2	1.6487	6506	6525	6544	6563	6582	6601	6620	6639	6658	2	4	6	8	10	11	13	15	17
5.3	1.6677	6696	6715	6734	6752	6771	6790	6808	6827	6845	2	4	6	7	9	11	13	15	17
5.4	1.6864	6882	6901	6919	6938	6956	6974	6993	7011	7029	2	4	5	7	9	11	13	15	17

* Reproduced from "Logarithmic and Other Tables," by Frank Castle, by kind permission of the publishers, Macmillan Company, Ltd., London.

(*Explanation is on page 251.*)

TABLE V.—NAPIERIAN LOGARITHMS.*—(Continued)

	0	1	2	3	4	5	6	7	8	9	Mean differences								
											1	2	3	4	5	6	7	8	9
5.5	1.7047	7066	7084	7102	7120	7138	7156	7174	7192	7210	2	4	5	7	9	11	13	14	16
5.6	1.7228	7246	7263	7281	7299	7317	7334	7352	7370	7387	2	4	5	7	9	11	12	14	16
5.7	1.7405	7422	7440	7457	7475	7492	7509	7527	7544	7561	2	3	5	7	9	10	12	14	16
5.8	1.7579	7596	7613	7630	7647	7664	7681	7699	7716	7733	2	3	5	7	9	10	12	14	15
5.9	1.7750	7766	7783	7800	7817	7834	7851	7867	7884	7901	2	3	5	7	8	10	12	13	15
6.0	1.7918	7934	7951	7967	7984	8001	8017	8034	8050	8066	2	3	5	7	8	10	12	13	15
6.1	1.8083	8099	8116	8132	8148	8165	8181	8197	8213	8229	2	3	5	6	8	10	11	13	15
6.2	1.8245	8262	8278	8294	8310	8326	8342	8358	8374	8390	2	3	5	6	8	10	11	13	14
6.3	1.8405	8421	8437	8453	8469	8485	8500	8516	8532	8547	2	3	5	6	8	9	11	13	14
6.4	1.8563	8579	8594	8610	8625	8641	8656	8672	8687	8703	2	3	5	6	8	9	11	12	14
6.5	1.8718	8733	8749	8764	8779	8795	8810	8825	8840	8856	2	3	5	6	8	9	11	12	14
6.6	1.8871	1.8886	1.8901	8916	8931	8946	8961	8976	8991	9006	2	3	5	6	8	9	11	12	14
6.7	1.9021	9036	9051	9066	9081	9095	9110	9125	9140	9155	1	3	4	6	7	9	10	12	13
6.8	1.9169	9184	9199	9213	9228	9242	9257	9272	9286	9301	1	3	4	6	7	9	10	12	13
6.9	1.9315	9330	9344	9359	9373	9387	9402	9416	9430	9445	1	3	4	6	7	9	10	12	13
7.0	1.9459	9473	9488	9502	9516	9530	9544	9559	1.9573	9587	1	3	4	6	7	9	10	11	13
7.1	1.9601	9615	9629	9643	9657	9671	9685	9699	9713	9727	1	3	4	6	7	8	10	11	13
7.2	1.9741	9755	9769	9782	9796	9810	9824	9838	9851	9865	1	3	4	6	7	8	10	11	12
7.3	1.9879	9892	9906	9920	9933	9947	9961	9974	9988	2.0001	1	3	4	5	7	8	10	11	12
7.4	2.0015	0028	0042	0055	0069	0082	0096	0109	0122	0136	1	3	4	5	7	8	9	11	12
7.5	2.0149	0162	0176	0189	0202	0215	0229	0242	0255	0268	1	3	4	5	7	8	9	11	12
7.6	2.0281	0295	0308	0321	0334	0347	0360	0373	0386	0399	1	3	4	5	7	8	9	10	12
7.7	2.0412	0425	0438	0451	0464	0477	0490	0503	0516	0528	1	3	4	5	6	8	9	10	12
7.8	2.0541	0554	0567	0580	0592	0605	0618	0631	0643	0656	1	3	4	5	6	8	9	10	11
7.9	2.0669	0681	0694	0707	0719	0732	0744	0757	0769	0782	1	3	4	5	6	8	9	10	11
8.0	2.0794	0807	0819	0832	0844	0857	0869	0882	0894	0906	1	3	4	5	6	7	9	10	11
8.1	2.0919	0931	0943	0956	0968	0980	0992	1005	1017	1029	1	2	4	5	6	7	9	10	11
8.2	2.1041	1054	1066	1078	1090	1102	1114	1126	1138	1150	1	2	4	5	6	7	9	10	11
8.3	2.1163	1175	1187	1199	1211	1223	1235	1247	1258	1270	1	2	4	5	6	7	8	10	11
8.4	2.1282	1294	1306	1318	1330	1342	1353	1365	1377	1389	1	2	4	5	6	7	8	9	11
8.5	2.1401	1412	1424	1436	1448	1459	1471	1483	1494	1506	1	2	4	5	6	7	8	9	11
8.6	2.1518	1529	1541	1552	1564	1576	1587	1599	1610	1622	1	2	3	5	6	7	8	9	10
8.7	2.1633	1645	1656	1668	1679	1691	1702	1713	1725	1736	1	2	3	5	6	7	8	9	10
8.8	2.1748	1759	1770	1782	1793	1804	1815	1827	1838	1849	1	2	3	5	6	7	8	9	10
8.9	2.1861	1872	1883	1894	1905	1917	1928	1939	1950	1961	1	2	3	4	6	7	8	9	10
9.0	2.1972	1983	1994	2006	2017	2028	2039	2050	2061	2072	1	2	3	4	6	7	8	9	10
9.1	2.2083	2094	2105	2116	2127	2138	2148	2159	2170	2181	1	2	3	4	5	7	8	9	10
9.2	2.2192	2203	2214	2225	2235	2246	2257	2268	2279	2289	1	2	3	4	5	6	8	9	10
9.3	2.2300	2311	2322	2332	2343	2354	2364	2375	2386	2396	1	2	3	4	5	6	7	9	10
9.4	2.2407	2418	2428	2439	2450	2460	2471	2481	2492	2502	1	2	3	4	5	6	7	8	10
9.5	2.2513	2523	2534	2544	2555	2565	2576	2586	2597	2607	1	2	3	4	5	6	7	8	9
9.6	2.2618	2628	2638	2649	2659	2670	2680	2690	2701	2711	1	2	3	4	5	6	7	8	9
9.7	2.2721	2732	2742	2752	2762	2773	2783	2793	2803	2814	1	2	3	4	5	6	7	8	9
9.8	2.2824	2834	2844	2854	2865	2875	2885	2895	2905	2915	1	2	3	4	5	6	7	8	9
9.9	2.2925	2935	2946	2956	2966	2976	2986	2996	3006	3016	1	2	3	4	5	6	7	8	9
10.0	2.3026																		

NAPIERIAN LOGARITHMS OF 10^{+n}

n	1	2	3	4	5	6	7	8	9
$\log_e 10^n$	2.3026	4.6052	6.9078	9.2103	11.5129	13.8155	16.1181	18.4207	20.7233

* Reproduced from "Logarithmic and Other Tables," by Frank Castle, by kind permission of the publishers, Macmillan Company, Ltd., London.

(*Explanation is on page 251.*)

			Values of n_1, the number of degrees													
		1		2		3		4		5		6		7	
P =		0.05	0.01	0.05	0.01	0.05	0.01	0.05	0.01	0.05	0.01	0.05	0.01	0.05	0.01
1		161	4,052	200	4,999	216	5,403	225	5,625	230	5,764	234	5,859	237	5,928
2		18.51	98.49	19.00	99.01	19.16	99.17	19.25	99.25	19.30	99.30	19.33	99.33	19.36	99.34
3		10.13	34.12	9.55	30.81	9.28	29.46	9.12	28.71	9.01	28.24	8.94	27.91	8.88	27.67
4		7.71	21.20	6.94	18.00	6.59	16.69	6.39	15.98	6.26	15.52	6.16	15.21	6.09	14.98
5		6.61	16.26	5.79	13.27	5.41	12.06	5.19	11.39	5.05	10.97	4.95	10.67	4.88	10.45
6		5.99	13.74	5.14	10.92	4.76	9.78	4.53	9.15	4.39	8.75	4.28	8.47	4.21	8.26
7		5.59	12.25	4.74	9.55	4.35	8.45	4.12	7.85	3.97	7.46	3.87	7.19	3.79	7.00
8		5.32	11.26	4.46	8.65	4.07	7.59	3.84	7.01	3.69	6 63	3.58	6.37	3.50	6.19
9		5.12	10.56	4.26	8.02	3.86	6.99	3.63	6.42	3.48	6.06	3.37	5.80	3.29	5.62
10		4.96	10.04	4.10	7.56	3.71	6.55	3.48	5.99	3.33	5.64	3.22	5.39	3.14	5.21
11		4.84	9.65	3.98	7.20	3.59	6.22	3.36	5.67	3.20	5.32	3.09	5.07	3.01	4.88
12		4.75	9.33	3.88	6.93	3.49	5.95	3.26	5.41	3.11	5.06	3.00	4.82	2.92	4.65
13		4.67	9.07	3.80	6.70	3.41	5.74	3.18	5.20	3.02	4.86	2.92	4.62	2.84	4.44
14		4.60	8.86	3.74	6.51	3.34	5.56	3.11	5.03	2.96	4.69	2.85	4.46	2.77	4.28
15		4.54	8.68	3.68	6.36	3.29	5.42	3.06	4.89	2.90	4.56	2.79	4.32	2.70	4.14
16		4.49	8.53	3.63	6.23	3.24	5.29	3.01	4.77	2.85	4.44	2.74	4.20	2.66	4.03
17		4.45	8.40	3.59	6.11	3.20	5.18	2.96	4.67	2.81	4.34	2.70	4.10	2.62	3.93
18		4.41	8.28	3.55	6.01	3.16	5.09	2.93	4.58	2.77	4.25	2.66	4.01	2.58	3.85
19		4.38	8.18	3.52	5.93	3.13	5.01	2.90	4.50	2.74	4.17	2.63	3.94	2.55	3.77
20		4.35	8.10	3.49	5.85	3.10	4.94	2.87	4.43	2.71	4.10	2.60	3.87	2.52	3.71
21		4.32	8.02	3.47	5.78	3.07	4.87	2.84	4.37	2.68	4.04	2.57	3.81	2.49	3.65
22		4.30	7.94	3.44	5.72	3.05	4.82	2.82	4.31	2.66	3.99	2.55	3.76	2.47	3.59
23		4.28	7.88	3.42	5.66	3.03	4.76	2.80	4.26	2.64	3.94	2.53	3.71	2.45	3.54
24		4.26	7.82	3.40	5.61	3.01	4.72	2.78	4.22	2.62	3.90	2.51	3.67	2.43	3.50
25		4.24	7.77	3.38	5.57	2.99	4.68	2.76	4.18	2.60	3.86	2.49	3.63	2.41	3.46
26		4.22	7.72	3.37	5.53	2.98	4.64	2.74	4.14	2.59	3.82	2.47	3.59	2.39	3.42
27		4.21	7.68	3.35	5.49	2.96	4.60	2.73	4.11	2.57	3.79	2.46	3.56	2.37	3.39
28		4.20	7.64	3.34	5.45	2.95	4.57	2.71	4.07	2.56	3.76	2.44	3.53	2.36	3.36
29		4.18	7.60	3.33	5.42	2.93	4.54	2.70	4.04	2.54	3.73	2.43	3.50	2.35	3.33
30		4.17	7.56	3.32	5.39	2.92	4.51	2.69	4.02	2.53	3.70	2.42	3.47	2.34	3.30
32		4.15	7.50	3.30	5.34	2.90	4.46	2.67	3.97	2.51	3.66	2.40	3.42	2.32	3.25
34		4.13	7.44	3.28	5.29	2.88	4.42	2.65	3.93	2.49	3.61	2.38	3.38	2.30	3.21
38		4.10	7.35	3.25	5.21	2.85	4.34	2.62	3.86	2.46	3.54	2.35	3.32	2.26	3.15
42		4.07	7.27	3.22	5.15	2.83	4.29	2.59	3.80	2.44	3.49	2.32	3.26	2.24	3.10
46		4.05	7.21	3.20	5.10	2.81	4.24	2.57	3.76	2.42	3.44	2.30	3.22	2.22	3.05
50		4.03	7.17	3.18	5.06	2.79	4.20	2.56	3 72	2.40	3.41	2.29	3.18	2.20	3.02
60		4.00	7.08	3.15	4.98	2.76	4.13	2.52	3.65	2.37	3.34	2.25	3.12	2.17	2.95
80		3.96	6.96	3.11	4.88	2.72	4.04	2.48	3.56	2.33	3.25	2.21	3.04	2.12	2.87
100		3.94	6.90	3.09	4.82	2.70	3.98	2.46	3.51	2.30	3.20	2.19	2.99	2.10	2.82
200		3.89	6.76	3.04	4.71	2.65	3.88	2.41	3.41	2.26	3.11	2.14	2.90	2.05	2.73
1,000		3.85	6.66	3.00	4.62	2.61	3.80	2.38	3.34	2.22	3.04	2.10	2.82	2.02	2.66
∞		3.84	6.64	2.99	4.60	2.60	3.78	2.37	3.32	2.21	3.02	2.09	2.80	2.01	2.64

Values of n_2

* Reproduced from "Statistical Methods," by kind permission of the author, Professor G. W. Snedecor,

TABLE OF F^*

of freedom of the greater variance

8		10		12		16		20		30		50		100		∞	
0.05	0.01	0.05	0.01	0.05	0.01	0.05	0.01	0.05	0.01	0.05	0.01	0.05	0.01	0.05	0.01	0.05	0.01
239	5,981	242	6,056	244	6,106	246	6,169	248	6,208	250	6,258	252	6,302	253	6,334	254	6,366
19.37	99.36	19.39	99.40	19.41	99.42	19.43	99.44	19.44	99.45	19.46	99.47	19.47	99.48	19.49	99.49	19.50	99.50
8.84	27.49	8.78	27.23	8.74	27.05	8.69	26.83	8.66	26.69	8.62	26.50	8.58	26.35	8.56	26.23	8.53	26.12
6.04	14.80	5.96	14.54	5.91	14.37	5.84	14.15	5.80	14.02	5.74	13.83	5.70	13.69	5.66	13.57	5.63	13.46
4.82	10.27	4.74	10.05	4.68	9.89	4.60	9.68	4.56	9.55	4.50	9.38	4.44	9.24	4.40	9.13	4.36	9.02
4.15	8.10	4.06	7.87	4.00	7.72	3.92	7.52	3.87	7.39	3.81	7.23	3.75	7.09	3.71	6.99	3.67	6.88
3.73	6.84	3.63	6.62	3.57	6.47	3.49	6.27	3.44	6.15	3.38	5.98	3.32	5.85	3.28	5.75	3.23	5.65
3.44	6.03	3.34	5.82	3.28	5.67	3.20	5.48	3.15	5.36	3.08	5.20	3.03	5.06	2.98	4.96	2.93	4.86
3.23	5.47	3.13	5.26	3.07	5.11	2.98	4.92	2.93	4.80	2.86	4.64	2.80	4.51	2.76	4.41	2.71	4.31
3.07	5.06	2.97	4.85	2.91	4.71	2.82	4.52	2.77	4.41	2.70	4.25	2.64	4.12	2.59	4.01	2.54	3.91
2.95	4.74	2.86	4.54	2.79	4.40	2.70	4.21	2.65	4.10	2.57	3.94	2.50	3.80	2.45	3.70	2.40	3.60
2.85	4.50	2.76	4.30	2.69	4.16	2.60	3.98	2.54	3.86	2.46	3.70	2.40	3.56	2.35	3.46	2.30	3.36
2.77	4.30	2.67	4.10	2.60	3.96	2.51	3.78	2.46	3.67	2.38	3.51	2.32	3.37	2.26	3.27	2.21	3.16
2.70	4.14	2.60	3.94	2.53	3.80	2.44	3.62	2.39	3.51	2.31	3.34	2.24	3.21	2.19	3.11	2.13	3.00
2.64	4.00	2.55	3.80	2.48	3.67	2.39	3.48	2.33	3.36	2.25	3.20	2.18	3.07	2.12	2.97	2.07	2.87
2.59	3.89	2.49	3.69	2.42	3.55	2.33	3.37	2.28	3.25	2.20	3.10	2.13	2.96	2.07	2.86	2.01	2.75
2.55	3.79	2.45	3.59	2.38	3.45	2.29	3.27	2.23	3.16	2.15	3.00	2.08	2.86	2.02	2.76	1.96	2.65
2.51	3.71	2.41	3.51	2.34	3.37	2.25	3.19	2.19	3.07	2.11	2.91	2.04	2.78	1.98	2.68	1.92	2.57
2.48	3.63	2.38	3.43	2.31	3.30	2.21	3.12	2.15	3.00	2.07	2.84	2.00	2.70	1.94	2.60	1.88	2.49
2.45	3.56	2.35	3.37	2.28	3.23	2.18	3.05	2.12	2.94	2.04	2.77	1.96	2.63	1.90	2.53	1.84	2.42
2.42	3.51	2.32	3.31	2.25	3.17	2.15	2.99	2.09	2.88	2.00	2.72	1.93	2.58	1.87	2.47	1.81	2.36
2.40	3.45	2.30	3.26	2.23	3.12	2.13	2.94	2.07	2.83	1.98	2.67	1.91	2.53	1.84	2.42	1.78	2.31
2.38	3.41	2.28	3.21	2.20	3.07	2.10	2.89	2.04	2.78	1.96	2.62	1.88	2.48	1.82	2.37	1.76	2.26
2.36	3.36	2.26	3.17	2.18	3.03	2.09	2.85	2.02	2.74	1.94	2.58	1.86	2.44	1.80	2.33	1.73	2.21
2.34	3.32	2.24	3.13	2.16	2.99	2.06	2.81	2.00	2.70	1.92	2.54	1.84	2.40	1.77	2.29	1.71	2.17
2.32	3.29	2.22	3.09	2.15	2.96	2.05	2.77	1.99	2.66	1.90	2.50	1.82	2.36	1.76	2.25	1.69	2.13
2.30	3.26	2.20	3.06	2.13	2.93	2.03	2.74	1.97	2.63	1.88	2.47	1.80	2.33	1.74	2.21	1.67	2.10
2.29	3.23	2.19	3.03	2.12	2.90	2.02	2.71	1.96	2.60	1.87	2.44	1.78	2.30	1.72	2.18	1.65	2.06
2.28	3.20	2.18	3.00	2.10	2.87	2.00	2.68	1.94	2.57	1.85	2.41	1.77	2.27	1.71	2.15	1.64	2.03
2.27	3.17	2.16	2.98	2.09	2.84	1.99	2.66	1.93	2.55	1.84	2.38	1.76	2.24	1.69	2.13	1.62	2.01
2.25	3.12	2.14	2.94	2.07	2.80	1.97	2.62	1.91	2.51	1.82	2.34	1.74	2.20	1.67	2.08	1.59	1.96
2.23	3.08	2.12	2.89	2.05	2.76	1.95	2.58	1.89	2.47	1.80	2.30	1.71	2.15	1.64	2.04	1.57	1.91
2.19	3.02	2.09	2.82	2.02	2.69	1.92	2.51	1.85	2.40	1.76	2.22	1.67	2.08	1.60	1.97	1.53	1.84
2.17	2.96	2.06	2.77	1.99	2.64	1.89	2.46	1.82	2.35	1.73	2.17	1.64	2.02	1.57	1.91	1.49	1.78
2.14	2.92	2.04	2.73	1.97	2.60	1.87	2.42	1.80	2.30	1.71	2.13	1.62	1.98	1.54	1.86	1.46	1.72
2.13	2.88	2.02	2.70	1.95	2.56	1.85	2.39	1.78	2.26	1.69	2.10	1.60	1.94	1.52	1.82	1.44	1.68
2.10	2.82	1.99	2.63	1.92	2.50	1.81	2.32	1.75	2.20	1.65	2.03	1.56	1.87	1.48	1.74	1.39	1.60
2.05	2.74	1.95	2.55	1.88	2.41	1.77	2.24	1.70	2.11	1.60	1.94	1.51	1.78	1.42	1.65	1.32	1.49
2.03	2.69	1.92	2.51	1.85	2.36	1.75	2.19	1.68	2.06	1.57	1.89	1.48	1.73	1.39	1.59	1.28	1.43
1.98	2.60	1.87	2.41	1.80	2.28	1.69	2.09	1.62	1.97	1.52	1.79	1.42	1.62	1.32	1.48	1.19	1.28
1.95	2.53	1.84	2.34	1.76	2.20	1.65	2.01	1.58	1.89	1.47	1.71	1.36	1.54	1.26	1.38	1.08	1.11
1.94	2.51	1.83	2.32	1.75	2.18	1.64	1.99	1.57	1.87	1.46	1.69	1.35	1.52	1.24	1.36	1.00	1.00

Collegiate Press, Iowa, 1937.

TABLE VII.—TABLE OF THE MINIMUM NUMBER OF REPLICATES NECESSARY TO DEMONSTRATE SIGNIFICANT TREATMENT DIFFERENCES AT THE 5 PER CENT POINT

Coefficient of variability: $\left(\dfrac{\sigma}{\text{mean}}\text{ per cent}\right)$

Difference between treatment means (per cent of mean value)	1	2	3	4	5	6	7	8	9	10	12	14	16	18	20	25	30
1	9	31	70	123	193	277	377	492	623	769							
2	4	9	19	31	49	70	95	123	156	193	277	377	492	623	769		
3	3	5	9	15	23	31	42	55	70	86	123	168	219	277	342	534	769
4	3	4	6	9	14	19	25	31	39	49	70	95	123	156	193	301	433
5		3	5	7	9	13	17	21	25	31	45	61	79	100	123	193	277
6		3	4	5	7	9	12	15	19	23	31	42	55	70	86	134	193
7			3	4	6	7	9	12	14	17	24	31	41	51	63	98	142
8			3	4	5	6	8	9	11	14	19	25	31	39	49	76	109
9			3	4	4	5	6	8	9	11	15	20	25	31	38	60	86
10			3	3	4	5	6	7	8	9	13	17	21	25	31	49	70
11			3	3	4	4	5	6	7	8	11	14	18	21	26	40	58
12			3	3	3	4	5	5	6	7	9	12	15	19	23	34	49
13				3	3	4	4	5	6	6	8	11	13	16	20	29	41
14				3	3	3	4	4	5	6	7	9	12	14	17	25	36
15				3	3	3	3	4	5	5	7	8	11	13	15	23	31
16				3	3	3	3	4	4	5	6	8	9	11	14	20	27
17				3	3	3	3	4	4	5	6	7	9	10	12	18	25
18					3	3	3	4	4	4	5	6	8	9	11	17	23
19					3	3	3	3	4	4	5	6	7	9	10	15	21
20					3	3	3	3	4	4	5	6	7	8	9	14	19
25						3	3	3	3	3	4	4	5	6	7	9	13
30							3	3	3	3	3	4	4	5	5	7	9
40										3	3	3	3	4	4	5	6
50											3	3	3	3	3	4	5

INDEX

A

Algebraic expressions for basic statistics, 28
  (*See also* Formulas; Analysis of variance)
Analysis of variance, 31*ff.*
  algebraic expressions for various forms of, 67–69, 167, 172
  complex, 58*ff.*
  skeleton, 206, 228
Assumed-mean method of statistical analysis, 24–26
  using several assumed means, 201–204
Average, arithmetical, 3, 97
  (*See also* Mean)

B

Binomial coefficients, 72
  tests of significance from, 75
Binomial expansion, 72, 98
  in testing statistical significance, 75, 76
  compared with t test, 76
Borders, nonexperimental, 161
  in perennial crop experiments, 193–195

C

Chi squared (χ^2), 70
  detailed analysis of, 83, 87
  formulas for calculating, 86
  number of degrees of freedom of, 71
    for contingency tables, 81
  significance of, 71
    when n (degrees of freedom) is large, 87
  table of, 250

Chi-squared test, 70*ff.*
  for homogeneity in a group of correlation coefficients, 117, 118
Class interval, 100, 102
  size of, 100
Coefficient, of correlation, 106
    (*See also* Correlation)
  of variation, 22–23
    calculation of, 23
    estimation of experimental precision from, 65
Complex experiments, 58, 208*ff.*
  advantages of, 66
  analysis of variance of, 206*ff.*
  confounded, 237–240
Confounded field experiments, 227*ff.*
  analysis of variance of, 229–235
    for 3^3 factorial design, 231–235
    for 2^3 factorial design, 229
  evaluation of confounded effects in, 233
  partial confounding in, 230
  with split plots, 238
Contingency table, 77
  calculation of χ^2 from, 77–81
    formula for, 79
  test of independence from, 77
Continuous variates, 2
Correction factor, 26
Correlation, 106*ff.*
  comparison with regression, 155
  dependent factor in, 121, 130, 137
  intraclass, 123
    (*See also* Intraclass correlation)
  negative, 105, 108
  partial, 119
    (*See also* Partial correlation)
  positive, 104, 108
Correlation coefficient, 106*ff.*
  calculation of, 107
    by short methods, 109–112

257